MAKING SENSE OF CLIMATE CHANGE

NEW LOOK AT CLIMATE THREATS AND REMEDIES

By

Don Whitmore

ISBN: 978-1-6657-1328-3 (sc)
ISBN: 978-1-6657-1329-0 (hc)
ISBN: 978-1-6657-1330-6 (e)

Library of Congress Control Number 2021920648

Table of Contents

Dedication

This book is dedicated to all who labor to halt global warming and enable global climate security.

Acknowledgement

Many friends, family and associates have helped to make this book possible. They have my deepest appreciation.

Alice Whitmore
Wilda Luttermoser
Fred Utter
Josie McGraw
Bill Whitmore
Cecilia Bitz
David Fowler
Jon Riedel
Brianna Abe
Joshua Huisenga
Hugh Fowler
Diana Gergel
Ronda Strauch
Megan Feddern

A special thanks to everyone quoted in the book. Your voice is important in helping to understand climate change, and that is no small contribution.

Graphics support by CHALKBOX CREATIVE

Preface

Federation Press Release

Subject: Contact with Planet Earth

Stardate: 7F9348 Translation: English

The galaxy-class cruiser Far Frontiers has landed on planet Earth. This first contact between Earthlings and Federation personnel became necessary due to conditions reported in the recently released Remote Audit of Humanoid Societies. Conditions on Earth, as determined by remote sensors, are (1) a high probability of self-destruction and (2) little evidence Earth's society is positioned to correct human-caused conditions risking such destruction. Also, Earth's society lacks reliance on common sense and rational reasoning.

The Federation is intervening to assure survival of Earth's habitat and to protect innocent humans from catastrophic events, such as mass starvation and nuclear war. Another objective is to assist Earth's society in managing its affairs safely, effectively and humanely.

Update reports from Far Frontiers are expected at thirty Earth-day intervals.

Science fiction? Yes. But it does raise the REAL question of what an independent audit of Earth's society might reveal.

Evidence of dangerous mismanagement of Earth's affairs is not difficult to find. Two examples are:

a. Overfishing wild stocks to the point of no return, while jeopardizing aquaculture (fish farming) production.

b. Keeping nuclear weapon arsenals, unnecessarily, on continuous "launch-on-warning" alert.

These examples are briefly explained in the following paragraphs.

Overfishing

Fish stocks have a limited natural capacity for supporting commercial fishing, called "maximum sustained yield." Overfishing a stock means that stock is no longer self-sustaining; commercial yields drop and ultimate survival is threatened. Currently, about 90% of global fish stocks are fished at or beyond their sustainable limits. In the 1970s, overfished stocks comprised 10% of all stocks, but in 2013 that percentage had more than tripled to 32%.[1] If this trend continues, wild fish stocks are headed towards near-extermination. A profound consequence would be the loss of genetic diversity needed to assure a robust species.[2] There is no certainty this trend will be slowed.

Illicit fishing accounts for much of the loss in fish stocks. Illegal, unreported and unregulated (IUU) fishing is estimated at 20–50% of the total catch.[3] For example, IUU industrial ships deploy "fish aggregating devices" (FADS) to maximize illegal catches. Many believe subsidies for the fishing industry (e.g., for fuel) enable such illicit fishing to thrive.[4] Hence, there are calls for subsidies to end. These annual subsidies exceed $35 billion worldwide.[5]

The aquaculture industry is also at risk because some species, such as salmon, are fed from diminishing open-sea catches. Further, the genetic diversity of farm fish is already severely compromised. Aquaculture may also suffer from shrinking marine biodiversity. For example, sea corals support one-fourth of all marine species, but are themselves headed for extinction by 2050 (or as early as 2030). Sea corals are being devastated by warmer oceans and greater carbon dioxide absorption by the oceans.

The combination of ocean fishing and aquaculture provides critical life support to 10% of the world's population.[6] Devastation of that industry would likely result in mass starvation and increased competition for remaining food supplies. Further, the loss of some 200 million jobs connected to the global fishing industry[7]would rock the world economy and ruin countless livelihoods. Depletion of fish stocks also compromises global biodiversity and Earth's ecosystems.[15]

Intelligent management of fish resources could avoid dire consequences. A robust fish population can be self-sustaining and can support regulated commercial fishing indefinitely. To be candid, it would be stupid to lose that important food source.

Launch-on-Warning Nuclear Weapons Alert

The United States and Russia have about 900 strategic nuclear weapons on 24/7 readiness for immediate launch against enemy targets.[8] The underlying scenario is that an enemy may be tempted to launch a nuclear first strike against its adversary. From the U.S. viewpoint, land radars and satellite sensors could give up to 30 minutes' warning before land-based ICBMs hit. Upon warning of an attack in progress, a quick launch of these missiles would assure retaliation against the enemy.[8] The premise is that the quick-launch capability of these ICBMs would deter an enemy from ordering a first strike.

This tortured reasoning is an artifact of Cold War nuclear policies and war-fighting strategies. It hinges on assumptions that are unverifiable. Nevertheless, this hair-trigger alert policy continues to be implemented. As will be briefly shown, the policy is both dangerous and unnecessary.

In the scenario summarized above, the U.S. President has some 3-6 minutes to decide whether to order a counterattack.[9] What if the warning is a false alarm, or the U.S. command and control system is hacked to create the illusion of a real attack? World War III might be the result, with nuclear casualties in the hundreds of millions.

False attack warnings have a real history. In 1979, U.S. command and control computers concluded a major Soviet missile attack was underway.[8] Nuclear weapon crews were ordered into action. When satellite sensors could not confirm the attack, weapon crews ceased launch preparations. These false attack warnings were generated by simulation training software.

In 1983, Soviet satellite sensors warned of incoming U.S. ballistic missiles.[8] A Soviet military official decided to take a chance that it was a false alarm, and a counterattack was not ordered. His instincts proved correct, but the margin of nuclear safety was razor-thin.

These harrowing tales underscore the need for cool heads and the highest degree of professionalism in missile launch crews. Two unfortunate incidents have cast a shadow over the proficiency of U.S. missile launch personnel. In January 2014, over 100 officers in the U.S. Air Force and Navy were charged with cheating on nuclear proficiency exams.[9] In March 2016, 14 airmen of the 90th Missile Wing (Wyoming) were disciplined for using the mind-bending LSD drug.[10]. The 90th Missile Wing commands 400 Minuteman ICBMs.

Regarding the threat of computer hacking mentioned earlier, a widely-recognized authority on nuclear weapons command and control, Dr. Bruce G. Blair, commented:

"Could a foreign agent launch another country's missiles against a third country? We don't know. Could a launch be set off by false warning data that had been corrupted by hackers? This is an especially grave concern."[11]

This hacking threat was greatly expanded recently when powerful hacking tools were stolen from the U.S. National Security Agency.[12] Defenses against hacking have been seriously compromised.

Dangers associated with nuclear weapons hair-trigger alert are risks not worth taking. Former Secretary of Defense William Perry warned, "The highest probability of starting a nuclear war is a mistaken launch caused by false alarm."[13] Daryl Kimball, Executive Director of the Arms Control Association, recently cautioned, "These dangerous launch-under-attack postures perpetuate the risk that false alarms could trigger a massive nuclear exchange."[14]

Given the expanded computer hacking threat, nuclear weapons should be taken off 24/7 alert now. Further, this alert policy for land-based ICBM's is unnecessary because the sea-based nuclear missile submarine force is clearly sufficient to deter an enemy first strike. Also, the nuclear weapons arsenal (including land-based ICBMs) is designed to withstand a massive attack.[14] The current ICBM alert policy makes no sense, and it increases risks to both national and global security.

If global overfishing and 24/7 nuclear weapon hair-trigger alert were the only threats to society, then these might seem manageable. Such is not the case. Society's problems are multiplying faster than effective solutions. Unchecked terrorism, baffling climate change, persistent civil wars, unaffordable health care, expanding poverty, chronic social injustices, sputtering economies, rising sea levels, daunting internet hacking, evolving exotic diseases, stubborn nuclear weapons proliferation, elusive migration justice, extreme weather events, skyrocketing drug abuse, record-breaking refugee populations, uneven law enforcement, formidable environmental pollution, growing urban homelessness and worsening wildfires are among additional challenges.

Serious problems deserve serious solutions. Practical, common-sense solutions should be more feasible if the situations are better understood. Making sense of the issues should lead to better understanding.

Which brings us to the subject of this book. Global warming and climate change are both poorly understood and are growing threats to society. Some four decades of situational awareness and public dialog have failed to produce consensus on how to manage the situation. Greater public understanding seems a necessary prerequisite to achieving such consensus and to enable commitment of the resources needed to combat the threat.

Global warming and climate change are subjects that could fill volumes. The emphasis in this book is to provide some basic background information together with thought-provoking assessments (including solution proposals). This information will, hopefully, contribute to public dialog and constructive debate. Such dialog and debate are probably necessary to build consensus on achievable solutions.

Making sense of climate change has been a rewarding challenge. One challenge has been in converting scientific jargon into plain English. One of the most rewarding experiences has been in discovering climate situations that have escaped widespread attention. The most significant discovery is the potential for a global flood of greenhouse gas emissions (rather than gradual reductions towards "net-zero")[16]. This situation is labeled "carbon emissions surge" and is explained in Chapter 2. The likelihood of such a surge depends mostly on society's choice between alternative climate futures. (Chapters 2 and10).

A surge in greenhouse gases would generate excess thermal energy that enables more severe and more frequent climate disasters. This potential situation is contrary to widely held expectations and it would challenge current notions on how to combat climate change.

Don Whitmore June 6, 2022

Sources

(1) Staff, "All the Fish in the Sea," The Economist, May 27, 2017, pp.22-24 (I2084)

(2) Dr. Fred M. Utter, Retired NOAA scientist and renowned fisheries geneticist, (Private conversation), November 1, 2017

(3) Staff, "Monsters of the Deep", The Economist, October 24, 2020, p.14 (I2915)

(4) Staff. "Piscine Plunder," The Economist, November 21, 2020, pp. 30-1 (I2931)

(5) Staff, "The Outlaw Sea," The Economist, October 24, 2020, pp.53-5 (I2914)

(6) Staff, "Deep Trouble," The Economist, May 27, 2017, p.18 (I2083)

(7) Mukhisa Kituyi and Peter Thomson, "90% of Fish Stocks are Used Up—Fisheries Subsidies Must Stop Emptying the Oceans," World Economic Forum, July 13, 2018, pp. 1-3 (I2935)

(8) Editors, "Take Nukes Off a Short Fuse," Scientific American, March 2017, p.10 (I2084)

(9) Patty-Jane Geller, "An Assessment of U.S. Military Power: U.S. Nuclear Weapons Capability," Heritage Foundation, November 17, 2020, pp. 1-35 (I2938)

(10) Robert Burns, "Security Troops on U.S. Nuclear Missile Base Took LSD," Associated Press, May 24, 2018, pp. 1-7 (I2934)

(11) Bruce G. Blair, "Why Our Nuclear Weapons Can Be Hacked," New York Times, March 14, 2017, pp.1-3 (I2070)

(12) Scott Shane et al., "Deep Security Breach Cripples N.S.A.," New York Times, November 13, 2017, pp. 1, 14

(13) Rebeccah Heinrichs, "Our ICBMs Are Necessary and No They Are Not on Hair-Trigger Alert," Real Clear Defense (Hudson Institute), p. 1-3 (I2937)

(14) Daryl Kimball, "Nuclear False Warning and the Risk of Catastrophe," Arms Control Today, December, 2019, p.3 (I2936)

(15) Amy McKeever, et. al., "How Overfishing Threatens the World's Oceans - and Why it Could End in Catastrophe", NationalGeographic.com, February 7, 2022, pp. 1-3 (I3133)

(16) Kelly Sims Gallagher, "The Coming Carbon Tsunami" Foreign Affairs, January/February 2022, pp. 151-164 (3125)

Introduction: Truth of the Matter

Is Global Warming Real?

According to some, global warming is a hoax. Others claim the warming is real. **The truth is** Earth is much warmer now than 200 years ago, when a long-term cooling trend was interrupted by a warming trend. Proof of this fact is provided in Chapters 1 and 2.

Chapter 1 describes how global warming is melting mountain glaciers across the globe. Ninety percent of such glaciers are losing mass faster than they are gaining new mass. Glacier devastation is happening at an alarming rate. For example, the number of glaciers (25 acres or larger) in Glacier National Park has shrunk from 150 to merely 26. The Humboldt glacier in Venezuela is near extinction. Mountain glaciers in the vicinity of Mt. Everest are also melting rapidly. Glaciers in Alaska's Denali National Park are now melting at a greater rate than at any time in recent history because of warmer summers. This is the current trend nearly everywhere, and rising temperatures will only accelerate the melting.

Can the Humboldt and other glaciers ever return to their former grandeur? Yes, if the warming trend is terminated and a long-term cooling trend is restored. Meanwhile, fresh water from mountain glacier sources—which supports agricultural production, hydroelectric power generation, fisheries habitat and human consumption—is destined to become a mere memory if glacier devastation is not arrested.

It should be noted global warming, itself, is happening extremely fast on a geological time scale, and severe impacts of climate change are already being felt. The notion that global warming is a slow-moving threat is a myth. Some climate change impacts, such as the melting rates of polar ice sheets, are accelerating. The "tipping point" collapse of these ice sheets could cause a catastrophic jump in worldwide sea levels. The risk of such surprise events is not known and cannot be known because of current limitations of science and technology.

Chapter 2 provides conclusive evidence of how much average global surface temperatures are rising and of the accelerated melting of snow and ice at the poles. This evidence, together with mountain glacier devastation evidence, is absolute proof of the global warming trend.

Chapter 2 also addresses future warming trends, including the possibility of a carbon emissions surge. Such a surge would profoundly impact global warming and climate change. That surge would depend on whether society takes immediate action to replace fossil fuels with clean energy sources.

What is Causing Global Warming?

Many believe human activity is a principal cause of global warming. Others assert that natural processes are to blame. This dispute is one factor polarizing the climate debate, and it has contributed to the lack of consensus on what to do about the climate change situation. **The truth is** global warming is caused by a combination of human activity and natural processes, as explained in Chapter 3. A summary explanation follows:

Heating of the atmosphere is caused by the interaction of thermal radiation on certain "greenhouse" gases. This is a natural process that normally keeps Earth habitable at a "Goldilocks" level: not too hot or too cold. However, human activity has disturbed the natural balance and allowed Earth's temperatures to rise to an unnatural level. A good example (discussed below) is carbon dioxide (CO_2), which is one of the greenhouse gases.

The amount of carbon dioxide in the atmosphere depends on a delicate balance between sources (which emit CO_2 into the atmosphere) and sinks (which absorb CO_2 from the atmosphere). Human activity has increased CO_2 sources and reduced CO_2 sinks, allowing carbon dioxide concentration in the atmosphere to rise to unnatural levels. CO_2 sources added by human activity are air pollution gases such as those from burning fossil fuels in power plants, motor vehicles, and aircraft. Reduced CO_2 sinks are trees logged for commercial, agricultural and consumer uses (trees absorb CO_2 from the air). This CO_2 sink reduction is also known as deforestation.

In short, human activity has produced excess CO_2 in the atmosphere, causing an unnatural level of atmospheric heating. Carbon dioxide levels are continuing to rise, and an unfortunate truth is that CO_2 has a reputation for lingering in the atmosphere for 1,000 years or more! Daily carbon dioxide emissions add to the long-term accumulations.

Additional greenhouse gases include water vapor and methane, whose concentrations in the atmosphere can also depend on both human activity and natural processes.

How Quickly Should Society Take Action to Terminate Global Warming?

The conventional wisdom has been that Earth is warming so slowly that urgent mitigation can wait a decade or so. Until recently, this was the position of the UN-affiliated Intergovernmental Panel on Climate Change (IPCC). In the IPPC's report issued in October 2018 there were finally warnings of dire consequences by 2040 if mitigation did not begin soon. **The truth is** global warming is already causing dire consequences, and serious mitigation should have begun long ago.

One reason for delay might be that the global warming threat is underestimated. First, attention is largely focused on the rise in average global atmospheric temperature near the surface. This atmospheric heating metric grossly misrepresents total global heating by a factor of nearly 15, because the oceans absorb 93% of the excess heat generated by the greenhouse effect. Second, global warming is triggering unstable conditions, which, in turn, can and do cause extreme and catastrophic events (explained in Chapter 4). Third, the current and potential threats of climate change appear to be widely misunderstood (addressed in Chapters 4 through 7).

Another factor behind mitigation delay might be public ignorance of the situation. First, there is an atmosphere of mutual distrust between scientists, politicians, and the general public. Second, there is little veracity of information on the subject: uninformed opinions seem to carry the same or more weight than authoritative consensus. Third, the sheer volume of information in the media obscures what little good information is available to the public. Fourth, much of society has ceased to read newspapers, magazines and books. Sources of information for many are the internet, tweets and blogs. Fifth, there is considerable apathy towards disturbing or "negative" subjects. Underlying all these factors is corrupted information (lies, fake news, etc.) that poisons the capacity to clarify issues and resolve differences of opinion.

Climate change is happening much faster than many realize. For example, conditions for plant growth are migrating poleward, causing a marked greening of the planet (observable from space satellites). Migrating animals include beavers, which are now found in regions of permafrost. The atmospheric jet stream and major ocean currents are significantly affected by global warming. These changes, in turn, affect local and regional weather, including extreme events. In other words, global warming threats are a current reality, and delays in serious mitigation invite continued severe impacts in the immediate future.

But what might be the most significant reason for foot-dragging on serious mitigation? The likely truth of the matter can be expressed in a brief narrative, starting here:

A principal cause of global warming and climate change is air pollution from burning fossil fuels. Serious mitigation would likely require restrictions on fossil fuel consumption, which would almost certainly be vigorously opposed by the fossil fuel industry. Some influential lawmakers in Congress might fear that their reelection depends on continued contributions from the fossil fuel industry. Thus, big money is probably at the root of opposition to expedited mitigation. The irony of this situation is that the economic costs of global warming are probably much bigger. End of narrative.

What is Society's Response to Climate Change?

The truth is society at large is falling short in taking effective action to halt global warming: actions are weak in comparison to the gravity of the growing threats. Reasons for a weak response probably include lack of consensus that the threat is real, plus lack of understanding that serious commitments must be made to slow down and terminate the warming trend. The response situation is addressed in Chapter 8.

In summary, responses to the threat are mixed. Some sectors of society are making bold efforts to combat climate change, while others are making only token efforts or are actually making matters worse. An example of the latter has been China's ambitious program to populate India and Africa with dozens of coal-fired power plants.

Responses to climate change threats cut across international entities, national and local governments, plus the private sector. Major obstacles to effective action are addressed in Chapter 9 and include institutional inertia, lack of constructive debate, human fallibility, and highly corrupted information.

What is the overall assessment of the global warming/climate change situation?

The truth is global warming is continuing without any proven practical plan to terminate the trend or any enforceable global commitment to provide necessary resources to implement such a plan. In short, climate change is a runaway threat. Evidence for this is provided in Chapters 4 through 7 and 10.

The basic reality is that society is failing to effectively manage the climate change situation. Current climate efforts are dangerously mismatched to the urgency and magnitude of growing threats. This mismatch, if not corrected, is destined to cause immense pain, suffering and loss of life for humanity in particular and for the biosphere in general. The very habitat for human society and all other life forms is at risk.

Are there practical remedies for the climate change situation?

Humanity's predicament, assessed in Chapter 10, should be viewed in a broad context. **The truth is** there are emerging technologies that can help rescue the situation, and human society has the potential for renewal in how it manages its affairs. Hydrogen fuel technology is an especially promising option for replacing fossil fuels as the dominant energy source. Chapter 11 outlines technology initiatives and climate action projects to begin serious mitigation of the escalating threats. Organizing for action and cost/funding issues are also addressed. Chapter 11 identifies reasons for optimism that climate change threats can be effectively countered.

What are possibilities for the future?

The practical remedies discussion is continued in Chapter 12. It can be argued that society is in need of renewal, and that solving urgent problems could give credence to a hopeful future. Chapter 12 makes this case for three urgent situations: climate change, overfishing and the hair-trigger "launch on warning" of nuclear weapons. The more distant future holds some amazing possibilities for coming generations. **The truth is** society can move boldly into a future marked by sustainable progress and equitable human welfare, *if it so chooses*.

Chapter 1: Mountain Glaciers and Global Warming

Introduction

Mountain glaciers around the world have been melting at accelerating rates for decades. In the first decade of the 21st century, the average global melt rate was twice the average rate during the previous 50 years[1]. A remarkable fact is that excessive glacial melting is occurring simultaneously in virtually every glaciated mountain range in the world, regardless of latitude or regional climate. Such synchronized and rapid global melting has only one reasonable explanation: global temperatures have been rising during this glacial meltdown. The common term for this unprecedented situation is "global warming."

Global warming and excessive glacier melting are bound together by cause and effect. Consequently, compelling evidence of excessive glacier melting on a global scale is conclusive proof of global warming. This chapter provides authoritative evidence of global devastation of mountain glaciers due primarily to global warming.

An important document on this subject was published in the Journal of Glaciology in 2015 and released on-line on July 10, 2017.[1] Titled "Historically unprecedented global glacier decline in the early 21st century," it is based on observational data compiled by the World Glacier Monitoring Service (WGMS). WGMS is *the* international organization for compiling and analyzing rigorous glacier data. A worldwide network of glacier monitoring specialists supports WGMS. The Director of WGMS is Michael Zemp, who is also the lead author of the journal document cited above. A few excerpts from that document follow:[1]

"Observations show that glaciers around the world are in retreat and losing mass. Internationally coordinated for over a century, glacier monitoring activities provide an unprecedented dataset of glacier observations from ground, air and space."

"The dataset...delivers clear evidence that centennial glacier retreat is a global phenomenon."

"Glacier fluctuations, i.e. changes in length, area, volume and mass,...are well recognized as high-confidence indicators of climate change (Bojinski and others, 2014)."

The four authors of this document cited over 120 authoritative references. Without doubt, this document represents an important benchmark that establishes the dynamic state of mountain glaciers and its connection to climate change. However, the scientific rigor of that document is likely difficult for lay consumption. This chapter attempts to help bridge that gap and provide a broader context for the mountain glacier situation (including impacts on communities and habitat downstream of the melting glaciers).

Mountain Glaciers 101

Mountain glaciers are a thing of beauty when crowning mountain peaks and following valleys down to lower elevations. Their retreat uphill also provides conclusive evidence of climate change caused by global warming. There is ample quantitative evidence to prove glaciers are shrinking, and such statistics are compelling, but perhaps not as compelling as visual evidence. The photographs on the next page (Figure 1-1) show the devastating effects of global warming.[2] Three different glaciers are pictured here but each is taken twice: once recently and the same glaciers about 100 years ago. This is called "repeat photography" because the recent photo is taken from the same vantage point as the earlier photo, yielding an accurate comparison before and after considerable shrinkage. Many such glacier comparisons have been catalogued.

An accepted definition of a glacier is a snow/ice mass that moves. This means the mass has grown large enough that it spreads under its own weight, and/or that its sheer weight can be pulled downhill by gravity against surface friction with the mountain terrain.

Mountain glaciers are unique physical features with interesting "personalities." For example, the snow/ice mix has "plastic" behaviors that allow some parts of the glacier mass to move at different speeds than other parts. Their massive weight sitting on steep slopes is constantly being pulled downhill by gravity. But friction with the underlying mountain surface (bedrock or other material) provides constant resistance to movement. According to the laws of physics, frictional forces are proportional to weight. So, the powerful forces of gravity are opposed by powerful frictional forces. The usual result is very slow glacier movement downhill (frictional forces are sometimes greatly reduced by lubricating water on the glacier's underside, allowing faster downhill speeds).

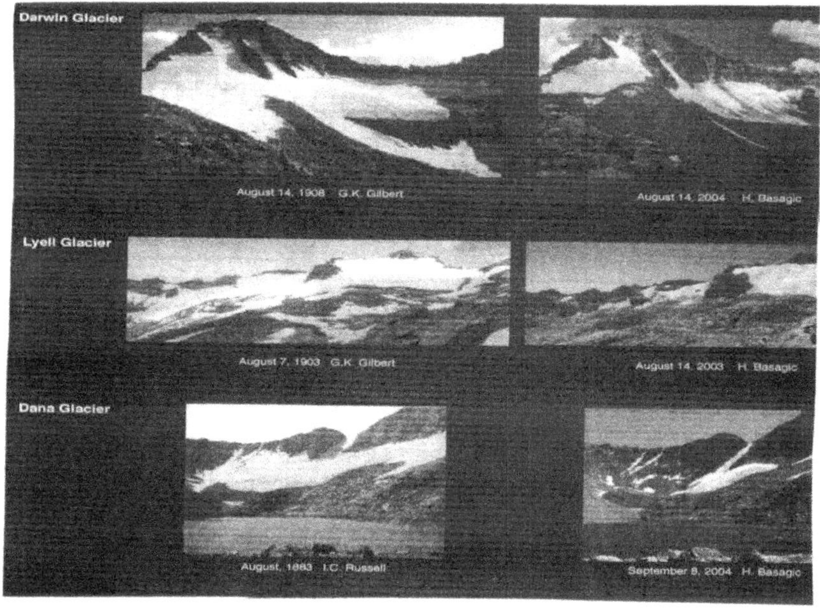

Figure 1-1 Repeat Photography -
Sierra Nevada Mountain Glaciers, U.S.A.

Glaciers also shrink and expand in the "tug-of-war" between cold weather snow accumulation and warm weather melting (glaciologists call this tug-of-war "mass balance"). Seasonal variations are normal for snow accumulation and ice melting. But global warming is pushing that tug-of-war uphill to the extent that many mountain glaciers have lost it, and are either becoming extinct or have already become extinct. The illustration on the next page (Figure 1-2) shows how a balanced tug-of-war moves up a mountain and glaciers below the new line of balance are in a "glacier extinction zone" (populated by those glaciers that are losing or have lost the tug-of-war).

The birth and growth of mountain glaciers is also of interest. Glaciers form when snow continues to accumulate in one place, such as on a mountaintop or in bowl-shaped terrain in the mountain topography. Glaciers themselves reshape mountain terrain by picking up loose boulders and rocks on their underside, which then scrape the mountain surface as the glaciers move downhill. During the last ice age, massive glaciers sculpted mountain and downslope terrain by carving out river valleys, lake bottoms, and sea floors. Today's mountain glaciers are generally remnants of those legacy glaciers.

Returning to glacier growth, over a long period of time the weight of snow accumulation compresses snow at greater depth, and this compression eventually increases ice crystal density to the point of becoming solid ice. As the glacial mass slowly moves downhill, new glacial mass accumulates above the moving glacier. During a long cooling trend, this snow/ice mass continues to thicken and to expand in breadth and length as it moves downslope. However, the glacier mass at lower elevations encounters warmer seasons, perhaps including more rainfall than snowfall. Meanwhile, the stress of moving over rough terrain contributes to deep cracks (crevasses) in the glacier's surface. These crevasses allow rainwater and snow/ice melt water to penetrate deeply into the glacier. Eventually, this water reaches the bottom of the glacier, where it lubricates the ground underneath. The heat generated by the movement of the glacier against friction probably adds melted water to the underside of the glacier. All this added lubrication reduces friction substantially, allowing the glacier mass to gain speed downhill.

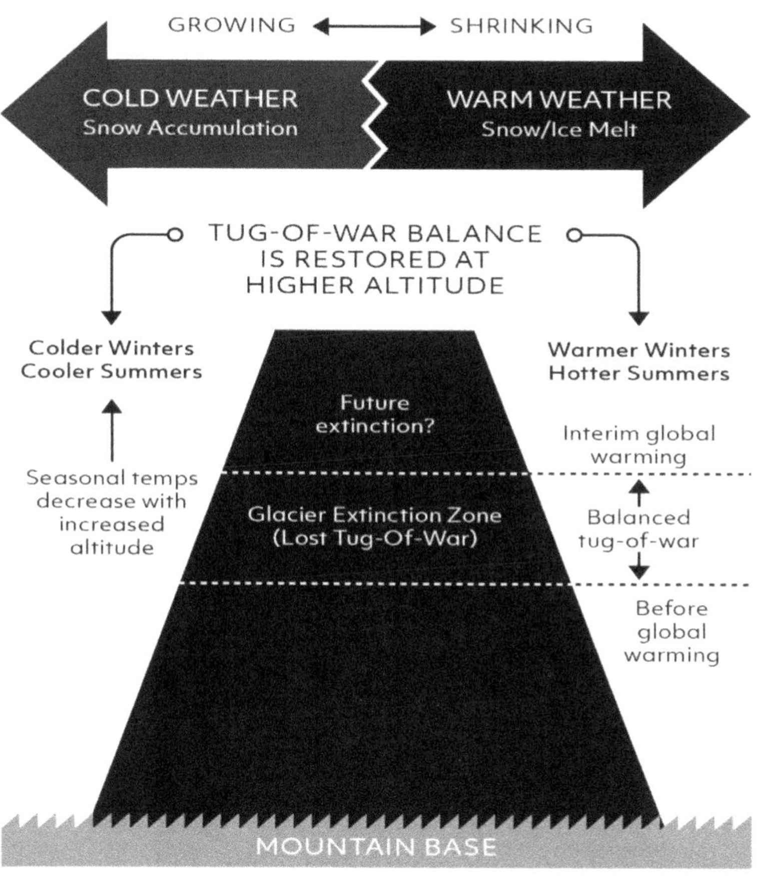

As one might imagine, glaciers are constantly changing, and the internal flow rate also varies between high and low elevations. This variability can translate to vulnerability to changing environments. Global warming compounds the vulnerability. Glacier variability can cause unstable conditions, leading to catastrophic events. Global warming can intensify environmental conditions by causing wetter and more frequent rainfall events. Several actual "tipping point" events are described in Chapter 4. These are events in which the lower end of a glacier detaches from the upper end, resulting in massive and fast avalanches—ones that exceed 200 miles per hour. These massive avalanches have occurred on low-gradient slopes, which is unprecedented in recorded history. Global warming may seem to be proceeding slowly, but its impacts can move at high speeds.

Regarding global warming impacts, shrinking glaciers are causing negative consequences for downstream communities, including metropolitan centers. Those consequences become dire when fresh water supplies dry up during extended droughts. Other victims of shrinking glaciers include hydroelectric energy output, agricultural production, fisheries habitats, and local economies. An expanded discussion on impacts follows the next section.

World-wide Status of Mountain Glaciers

The benchmark journal document discussed earlier provides a global assessment of retreating glaciers, which makes the connection with global warming. That composite assessment is authoritative proof that global warming is not a hoax. But a non-specialist may be put off by scientific jargon and remain unconvinced. If one were to make a world tour of glaciated mountain ranges, they could not escape the fact that glaciers are shrinking dramatically nearly everywhere. The same conclusion might be reached by someone reading this chapter. A tour of the world's glaciers is provided here. This tour surveys the status of glacier changes and includes a global "town hall" discussion on the mountain glacier situation. This collection of personal reflections is a value added to this book, and it may be an important adjunct to the glacier statistics. The tour begins here.

Arctic and Near-Arctic Mountain Glaciers

Global warming effects in the Arctic region are so severe as to transform the old climate (dominated by ice and snow) to a new climate, noted for "open water and rain."[3] This is the conclusion of a Fall 2020 report authored by the National Center for Atmospheric Research (Boulder, Colorado). This new climate reality is also explained by graphic charts in an August 2019 Scientific American article.[4] The profound transformation in Arctic climate helps explain why glaciers in the region are in such sustained retreat. Specific evidence is provided in this section.

Land areas in this region include Greenland, Iceland, the Yukon, Alaska, northern Russia, and northern Scandinavian countries. The status of mountain glaciers is summarized in that order.

GREENLAND

Over the last 15 years, Greenland's largest glacier has lost more ice than in the previous 100 years.[5] Eric Rignot, professor at the University of California, Irvine, remarked on a recent visit to Greenland: "None of us expected to see such changes in Greenland."[5] Recent ice losses in Greenland continue the rapid melting trend. The Spring thaw in 2019 began several weeks earlier than expected,[6] and by year end, Greenland's ice-sheet melt set a new 1-year record of over half a trillion metric tons.[7]

Besides air temperature increases, researchers have discovered that warm Atlantic currents are contributing to rapid glacier melting.[5] It should be noted that global warming adds heat to both the atmosphere and the oceans—especially to the oceans.

Other recent research has determined that geothermal activity from under Greenland's glaciers contributes to both melting and faster sliding towards the sea.[8] Greenland's glaciers are difficult to monitor on the ground due to logistical challenges.[9] Only 5 out of 20,000 peripheral glaciers and ice caps are currently monitored on the ground.[9] However, satellite monitoring is able to accurately measure Greenland's collective ice losses.

ICELAND

Glaciers in Iceland are melting rapidly and are destined to become extinct if global warming continues.[10] Laser measurements of glacier thickness find an average annual loss of more than one meter.[10] Hofsjo glacier is melting faster than all others, losing 100 meters in thickness between 1986 and 2015. Glacier melting rates in Iceland are "unprecedented in the recent geological history" according to To'mas Johannesson, a geophysicist at the Icelandic Meteorological Office.[10] A August 2019 ceremony in western Iceland was to unveil a plaque commemorating the Okjukull glacier—the first of Iceland's glaciers to suffer extinction. The plaque reads:

"In the next 200 years all our glaciers are expected to follow the same path. This monument is to acknowledge that we know what is happening and what needs to be done. Only you know if we did it."[11]

An interesting aspect of melting glaciers in Iceland is that the weight reduction is allowing the surface beneath the glacier to rise.[12] Richard Bennett, Associate Professor of Geosciences at the University of Arizona, attributes this effect to thinning glaciers and global warming.[12]

YUKON, CANADA

According to Professor Gwenn Flowers, a glaciologist at Simon Fraser University (Vancouver, British Columbia), Canada is home to about one-third of the world's mountain glaciers. Flowers spends summers measuring glaciers in the St. Elias mountain range in the Yukon.[13] She and other researchers are convinced the dramatic melting of the Yukon's glaciers is a warning of the climate change threat to the planet. One large glacier she is helping to map, the Kaskawulsh, is suffering from both melting and reduced snow accumulation.[13] This glacier, like so many others, is losing the mass balance battle. The Kaskawulsh lost 17 square kilometers of ice between 1977 and 2007. Professor Flowers adds, "What the glaciers and ice sheets do makes a big difference to global sea levels, and makes a big difference to local environments where they form a water source."[13]

A recent event illustrating climate changes in the Arctic region was a complete fracture of an ice shelf off northwestern Ellesmere Island.[14] A 31-square-mile slab broke off Milne ice shelf in late July 2020 and split again within a week. Remnants are now huge icebergs adrift in the Arctic Ocean. Summer temperatures in the area hover near freezing.[14]

ALASKA

A new study by the American Geophysical Union found that rising summer temperatures are melting glaciers in Alaska's Denali National Park faster than at any time in the last 400 years.[15] Ice cores taken from Mt. Hunter show that summer temperatures are up by as much as 2°C (3.6°F). Summer warming in the mountains is about double that at sea level.[15] The study also found this Arctic warming "correlates with hotter temperatures in the tropical Pacific Ocean."[15] These hotter tropical temperatures are changing how tropical water is transported to the poles. Dominic Winski, lead author of the study and a glaciologist at Dartmouth College, interpreted this phenomenon as showing how human-caused global warming is behind the fact that "temperature and precipitation patterns are different today than they were during the preindustrial period."[15]

NORTHERN RUSSIA

Recent research in the Russian Arctic has discovered the rate of glacier melting has doubled in the last 10 years compared to the previous 60 years.[16] Shrinking glaciers have even uncovered at least one new island, according to lead researcher Whyjay Zheng. The water equivalent of ice lost in the study area (Franz Josef Land in the Kava and Barets seas) would raise the largest of New York's Finger Lakes by 85 feet, inundating the cities of Ithaca and Seneca Falls.[16] Researcher Zheng remarked, "The temperature is changing in the Arctic faster than anywhere else in the world."

A different study in the area of the Russian Arctic (the Varilov Ice Cap) discovered the movement of that ice cap had accelerated from 2 inches per day to as much as 82 feet per day.[17] This case of instability exemplifies the accelerated dynamics in the Arctic glaciers and ice sheets.

Maria Ananicheve, a Russian glaciologist, summarized the condition of many Russian glaciers:[18] The rate of accumulation of snow and ice is already less than the rate of melting. The degradation is complete."[18] An immediate concern from the rapid melting is massive flooding over the next 20 years.[18]

NORTHERN SCANDINAVIAN COUNTRIES

The only remaining mountain glaciers are in Norway and Sweden. According to climate researchers, Norway will lose 98% of all its glaciers in the next 100 years.[19] It is expected that 11 out of 34 of its largest glaciers will fully retreat. Some 1600 glaciers will disappear completely.[19] These predictions were made at the Bjerkness Center for Climate Research at the University of Bergen and were published in the climate journal Cicerone.

The Norwegian Water Resources and Energy Directorate (NVE) measured 36 glaciers in 2018, of which 30 had shrunk, four remained unchanged and two had a net gain in mass.[20] All measured glaciers have shrunk since monitoring began in 1900, according to Rune Engeset, head glaciologist at NVE. [20]

Sweden's mountain glaciers are melting under record-breaking heat.[21] Martin Heberg, meteorologist at Swedish Weather and Climate Center, told Agence France-Press (AFP) that "temperature differences between the Arctic and the Mediterranean are narrowing." He also noted that globally, "extreme heat is 100 times more common today than it was during the 50's, 60's, and 70's." [21] Swedish researchers were alarmed recently when a prominent glacier on Mt. Kebnekaise melted so much it lost its status as Sweden's highest point. Dr. Gunhild Ninis Rosqvist, a professor at Stockholm University, remarked, "This glacier is a symbol for all glaciers in the world. This whole environment is melting ... and it affects the entire ecosystem." [21]

Northern Mid-Latitudes

Land areas in this region (which have glaciated mountains) include Canada, the United States of America, Europe, Asia, and the Middle East. The current status of mountain glaciers is summarized in that order.

CANADA

The Yukon has already been discussed under Arctic regions. Mid-latitude Canada has impressive mountain glaciers in the British Columbia and Alberta provinces. British Columbia, on Canada's west coast, has approximately 17,000 glaciers and interior Alberta has about 800.[22]

Glaciers in Western Canada averaged approximately 11% loss of their total surface area in the 20-year period ending in 2005.[23] The surface area loss on the drier eastern slopes of the Canadian Rockies exceeded 20%. Future loss of mass volume on those slopes could be 40–80% by the year 2100, depending on the assumed climate change scenario.[23] These estimates are from a 2018 report titled "Alberta Glacier inventory and Volume Estimation" by Shawn Marshall and Eric White.

Another study, published in the journal Nature Geoscience, calculated a 70% loss of glacier ice in Western Canada by 2100 "due to warming temperatures."[24] Co-author Garry Clarke, Professor Emeritus at the University of British Columbia, remarked in an interview: "The retreat or shrinkage of mountain glaciers is a world-wide phenomenon." He added that glacier ice losses in the drier Rockies could reach 90% by year 2100.[24]

USA (except Alaska and Hawaii)

Washington State in the Pacific Northwest is the most glaciated state in the continental United States.[25] Most of the glaciers are in three national parks: Olympic, North Cascades and Mt. Rainier. These parks generally offer visitor access to some of the glaciers, at least by hiking trails.

Blue glacier on Mt. Olympus in Olympic National Park is one of the most-studied glaciers in the world.[26] Global warming is taking its toll: Blue glacier has retreated 325 feet in 20 years (1995–2015).[25] Olympic National

Park had 266 glaciers in 1982, but only 184 by 2009. The North Cascades and Mt. Rainier are experiencing similar rapid melting. For example, glaciers in the North Cascades National Park decreased 7% in surface area between 1958 and 1998 (before the rapid melting of the 21st century).[27] The North Cascades is featured later in a profile of the Skagit River watershed. This profile exemplifies the dynamic impacts of global warming on communities situated downstream of melting glaciers.

East of Washington State are Idaho, Montana and Wyoming. Idaho had numerous glaciers in the last Ice Age, but likely no true (moving) glaciers remain. There are no named glaciers in Idaho, but it has some 208 glacier-like snow/ice patches (mostly in the Sawtooth mountain range in the central part of the state). [28]

Montana, however, is intersected by the Rocky Mountain range and is home to the renowned Glacier National Park (GNP). This park is a historic tourist destination that touts expansive lodges built by the passenger railroads. Unfortunately, GNP is not immune to global warming. Historic photographs reveal GNP once had 150 glaciers with surface areas larger than 25 acres. That number has melted down to only 26.[29] The average surface area shrinkage of all GNP glaciers was 39% between 1966 and 2015.[30] These statistics are from a joint study by the U.S. Geological Survey (USGS) and Portland State University (PSU). PSU geologist Andrew Fountain has remarked that this glacier melting "is in line with trends that have been happening on a global scale." [29]

Wyoming is also intersected by the Rocky Mountains, and there are several glaciated ranges in the state. There are 38 named glaciers plus some 1,400 permanent snow/ice bodies in Wyoming.[31] (The 38 glaciers are scattered across four mountain ranges: Wind River, Teton, Bighorn and Absaroka. Outside Washington State, seven of the ten largest glaciers in the Northwest corner of the United States are in the Wind River range.[31] The Wyoming glaciers have been generally retreating since the early 20th century.

Receding glaciers from global warming are producing noticeable changes in the Wind River range. Professor Darren Wells of Central Wyoming College observed from a research camp by the Dinwoody glacier: "Every year, more grass, less snow."[32] In the 50-year period beginning in 1950, measurements of the Dinwoody glacier surface area indicate it had shrunk from 850 acres to 540 acres. A 2011 study of aerial photographs of the Wind River glaciers estimated they lost 38% of their surface area in the last half of the 20th century.[32]

Due south of Washington State is Oregon and California. Like Washington, their glaciers benefit from moist westerly winds from the Pacific Ocean that deposit liberal amounts of snow in the mountains.

Oregon's glaciers are found on Mt. Hood, in the Cascades mountain range and in the Wallowa mountains (in northeastern Oregon). Oregon has 35 named glaciers, including 12 on Mt. Hood, four on Mt. Jefferson, and a total of 15 in the Sister mountains. [33]. An example of extensive glacier melting is Whitewater Glacier on Mt. Jefferson, whose surface dimensions have shrunk from 2x5 miles in 1917 to 0.6x1.9 miles today[33].

An on-site report on Oregon's glaciers from a glacier cave explorer Brent McGregor, summarized the situation: "A lot of ice is melting away very quickly, whether on polar caps, the glacier caves...but around the world we are seeing a lot of loss of ice."[34]

Twenty glaciers have been named in California—seven on Mt. Shasta and 13 in the Sierra-Nevada mountain range (among some 800 small glaciers mapped by the USGS) [35]. A geologist at Portland State University, Hassan Basagic, recently estimated the number of true glaciers in the Sierra-Nevada range at 118 "based on theoretical considerations."[2] A thesis he completed in 2011 quantified glacier changes in the Sierra-Nevada range caused by climate change. Surface areas of 14 studied glaciers shrank an average of 55% in the 20th century. The least shrinkage among the 14 was 31% and the greatest was 78%.[36] Basagic cited a reference that concludes, "Over the 20th century, with few exceptions, alpine glaciers have been receding throughout the world in response to a warming climate."[36]

Outside of Washington, Oregon, California, Montana, and Wyoming, only Colorado has a significant number of true (moving) glaciers. Colorado has 14 named glaciers, all of which are in the Front Range of the Rocky Mountains [37]. Eight of the named glaciers are in Rocky Mountain National Park (RMNP). The web page for RMNP summarizes glacier changes by noting, "since the 1990s[,] almost all glaciers have shown a retreat due to high rates of increasing summer temperatures ...This pattern of twentieth century fluctuations in mass is similar to that seen by glaciers across North America and globally."[38]

The Denver Post reported findings of scientists measuring shrinking glaciers with ground-penetrating radar.[39] The lead author of that study, hydrologist Mark Williams, also remarked on the fate of Glacier National Park: "Glacier National Park is not going to have glaciers in another couple decades. People are going to be upset about that. We're in a loop we cannot get out of."[39] This sentiment was reinforced by Colorado State University scientist Dan McGrath: "It's sad to say, but most mountain glaciers are predicted to be gone by the end of the century."[40]

EUROPE

Europe's glaciers in the northern mid-latitudes are found in the Alps and in Spain's Pyrenees mountains. Spain is quickly losing its glaciers. Between 1900 and 2019, their total surface area shrank from 3,300 hectares to only 390 hectares. Scientists expect them to be completely gone "within a few decades."[41] These scientists also warn the absence of glacier water sources during summer months could have "dramatic effects" on agriculture.[41]

The European Alps lost 50% of total glacial volume between 1850 and 1975, plus an additional 35–40% between 1975 and 2007.[42] Climate change is affecting weather patterns, resulting in "warmer winters and lower snow accumulation."[42] The other side of the glacier mass equation is accelerated melting due to "rising global temperatures."[42] The combination of less snow accumulation and more rapid melting is the basic cause of the devastating loss statistics cited above. This combination can also produce a tipping point beyond which glacial losses become virtually irreversible.

Even a single glacier can have a tipping point, as shown in Chapter 4. The Alps has a large glacier that seems to be approaching collapse due to a growing crevasse.[43] The Planpincieux glacier in northwestern Italy has a block of ice measuring some 9 million cubic feet that is threatening to separate from the glacier. "A collapse that big could reach the bottom of the valley" in the opinion of Daniele Giordan, a geologist at the Italian National Research Council.[43] Dr. Giordan has acknowledged that rising temperatures probably have a role in making the glaciers less stable.

ASIA

Glaciated mountains in Asia stretch between northwest Asia (Tien Shan and Hindu Kush) and southeast Asia (eastern Himalayas).[44] It should be noted these glaciers are an important fresh water source for over 1 billion people.[45]

According to a study published on September 13, 2017 in Nature, at least one-third of these glaciers will be gone by the year 2100.[46] Glacier losses could reach two-thirds if nothing is done to control global warming.[47] More recent studies confirm the accelerated rate of Himalayan glacier melt.[48] For example, the melt rate has doubled since year 2000, compared to the rate in the 1975–2000 period. This measurement was derived from satellite image analysis of over 650 glaciers across 1,200 miles of the Himalayas.[48]

Keeping global warming below a 1.5°C-rise above pre-industrial levels (as targeted by the 2015 Paris Accord) is "an ambitious goal."[49] Odds of curbing warming at this level are estimated to be about 1 in 100.[50] With warming to 3.5°C, Asia's glaciers could shrink 49%.[50] Known as the "Hindu Kush Himalaya Assessment," this comprehensive study was updated and released again on February 4, 2019.[51]

Receding glaciers can translate to fresh water shortages affecting croplands and human consumption. Such consequences are not hypothetical—parched farmlands are forcing an exodus from Nepalese villages.[52] One remaining villager remarked: "I love this village but I can't survive here much longer" (from an April 6, 2020 newspaper account).[52]

JAPAN

Three glaciers have been found in the Hida mountain range (Toyama Prefecture). One glacier is on Mt. Tateyama and two are on Mt. Tsurugi[53]. Their movement was measured at 10–30 cm per month. The glaciers are 27–30 meters thick and 400–1,200 meters long.[53] The glacier on Mt. Tate has been mentioned as one at risk due to climate change: "Sadly, these rare glaciers are becoming more threatened with each passing year."[54]

Tropical Latitudes

Glaciated lands at tropical latitudes include South America, New Guinea, and Africa.

SOUTH AMERICA

Equatorial glaciated mountains along the spine of the Andes are found in Venezuela, Colombia, Bolivia, Ecuador, and Peru. Venezuela is on the brink of losing its last surviving glacier: the Humboldt.[55] In contrast, Venezuela had four square miles of total glacier area in 1910.[56] This history of glacier devastation in South America is consistent with climate change predictions.[57]

Colombia has six remaining glaciers, but all are expected to be gone within 30 years if current melt rates continue.[58] Jorge Luis Ceballos, a research scientist at Colombia's National Institute of Hydrology, Meteorology and Environmental Studies, reports that "[i]n the last six years there has been total disequilibrium."[59]

Bolivia's glaciers are melting rapidly, and a persistent drought has prompted its government to declare a state of emergency.[60] Bolivia's two largest cities, La Paz and El Alto, depend on the Andean glaciers for much of their water supply. Between 1986 and 2014, Bolivian glaciers have shrunk 43%.[48] A growing concern is that the large lakes below the glaciers, impounded by fragile dams, are subject to catastrophic failure.[61]

Ecuador is home to the only mountain on Earth whose glaciers are intersected by the Equator: 19,000 ft. elevation Mt. Cayambe.[62] Glaciers on this mountain have retreated 50% in the last 30 years, and are predicted to all disappear within 20 years. [62] Ecuador's glaciers have suffered an average loss of 30% in the last 30 years, and all are expected to be gone in 70 years at current melt rates.[63]

Peru is also intersected by the majestic Andes and has glaciated mountains at tropical latitudes. Nearly half of the glacier mass in the Cordillera de Vilcanota range has disappeared since the mid-1970s.[64] All its glaciers are "likely to disappear" as global temperatures continue to rise.[64]

Peru is home to 70% of the world's tropical glaciers, and these are retreating at "an alarming rate."[65] They have lost about 40% of surface area since the 1970s.[65] A longtime resident of the mountain region, Americo Gonzalezz Caldua, has observed that the ice retreats uphill 20 yards each year as temperatures rise[66] He recently declared to a reporter: "Before, we saw our glaciers as beautiful, our mountain range covered in a white sheet that was stunning...But today, we don't see that any more on our glaciers, which we're losing more of every day. Instead of white, we are seeing stone." [66]

NEW GUINEA

New Guinea glaciers are extremely rare examples that exist at eastern tropical latitudes. However, scientists predict they will disappear within a decade.[54] Andrew Klein, a geography professor at Texas A&M University, notes, "Glacier recession continues in the tropics—these happen to be the last glaciers in the eastern tropics."[67] Five named ice masses in the Sudirman range were counted by space surveillance in 1988, but only two remained in the 2017 images.[67]

AFRICA

Glaciers in Africa have lost 80% of their surface area since 1900 due to both rising temperatures and decreasing atmospheric moisture.[68] These glaciers are all in East Africa: on Mt. Kenya, on Mt. Kilimanjaro, and on the

Ruwenzori range (Uganda and the Democratic Republic of Congo).[69] Deforestation on Mt. Kilimanjaro is probably responsible for drier conditions creating reduced snow accumulation.[70]

Southern Mid-Latitudes

Mountain glaciers at southern mid-latitudes are found only in the Andes range in South America - in central Chile and Argentina. A reliable water supply from the Andes is critically important to the ten million people in Santiago, Chile's capital. This was especially true in late summer and autumn of 2009–2010, which was notably dry.[71] Universidad glacier, the largest in central Chile, increased stream flow nearly 20% during that critical period. Loss of such fresh water sources due to shrinking glaciers is a global threat that has already become dire in some downstream communities.

The climate of the central Andes is semi-arid, with generous winter precipitation but rare summer rainfall.[72] This climate is often compared with the Mediterranean climate, as it has strong solar radiation in the summer, with low relative humidity. Glaciers are much larger than in northern Chile, but are shrinking noticeably. Three major glaciers shrank between 2.4% and 10.9% during the 1955–2006 interval.[72] One prominent glacier, the Echaurren Norte, lost 65% of its surface area between 1955 and 2015. It also split into two ice bodies in the late 1990s.[73] There is concern this glacier "may disappear in coming years" if the current devastation continues.[73]

Southern Sub-Polar Latitudes

South America is not alone in having glaciated mountains at these latitudes. The "Southern Alps" in New Zealand are also glaciated and happen to be at the same latitudes as Patagonia in southern Chile and Argentina. Although separated by 100 degrees longitude, being near the South Pole, these mountains are only hours apart by aircraft flying a great circle route.

SOUTH AMERICA

Chile and Argentina are home to Patagonia, which straddles the high Andes. A popular tourist destination, Patagonia also has the world's third-largest ice field (exceeded only by Greenland and Antarctica). A study of 270 of Chile's and Argentina's largest glaciers was released in April 2011.[74] Among findings, these glaciers have suffered accelerated losses of volume in the last 30 years: "10 to 100 times faster humidity, which has been found to increase glacier melt rate."[75] Referring to unprecedented changes in the Andes, Eric Rignot, a glaciologist at NASA's Jet Propulsion Laboratory, commented: "They are, in fact, melting away at some of the highest rates on the planet."[76]

NEW ZEALAND

New Zealand has some 3,000 glaciers, mostly on the South Island. Except for brief periods of glacier mass growth, these glaciers have been retreating since 1890. [77] Current changes are being monitored by scientists at Victoria University of Wellington's Antarctic Research Centre. Lauren Vargo at this center is building digital models of the glaciers based on historic photos and new photos taken by aerial photogrammetry. Digital processing allows glacier measurements that otherwise require researchers to be on site. It also allows accurate measurements to be made for inaccessible locations. Dr. Vargo finds "a retreat in almost all the glaciers we've studied."[78] She adds, "Globally, glaciers are one of the largest contributors to sea level rise and in New Zealand they are tourism icons and provide water to our major rivers. For these reasons, melting glaciers are a serious problem."[78]

Antarctica

This world tour of mountain glaciers concludes on an ice sheet that covers 98% of an entire continent.[79] Beyond the continental crust are floating ice shelves, into which mountain glaciers flow. These ice shelves encircle 75% of the Antarctica coast and help contain the glacier flow.[79] Beneath the ice sheet (which is four kilometers thick in places) are mountains and valleys. Here and there, mountain peaks rise above the ice sheet and provide some ice-free areas.

Two mountain ranges underlie the Antarctica ice sheets: the Gamburtser Range, under the East Antarctic Ice Sheet, and the Transantarctic Range, which divides East and West Antarctica. There are also sub-glacial lakes that are liquid despite the cold, and these help lubricate sheet movement across the terrain. The East Antarctic ice sheet rides on ground, above sea level, but the base of the West Antarctic ice sheet (along with associated glaciers) slides under the ocean's surface.[79]

Antarctica, twice the size of Australia, might seem to be a still, frozen wilderness. However, the vast landscape of ice is on the move. Aside from the many glaciers moving towards the sea and calving into coastal waters, the ice shelves are collapsing; glaciers are thinning and accelerating; ice sheets are sliding towards the sea and sea levels are rising.[80] The expansive Larsen C Ice Shelf collapsed dramatically in 2002 after being stable for 10,000 years.[80] Another dramatic loss of an Antarctic ice shelf occurred in Fall 2019 when Amery Ice Shelf shed a 610-square-mile iceberg, dubbed D28.[82] D28 is larger than Oahu, Hawaii.

Until recently, most of the dynamic changes have been in West Antarctica, while the vast and unexplored East Antarctic has been relatively stable. Now, there is a new dynamic that affects both West and East coastlines, and it is amplifying ice melt rates.[82] The new reality is that warm ocean water now reaches ice sheets, shelves, and glaciers. Before, the ocean water was chilled by "pre-mixing" with ice melt runoff. Now, it slides under stratified ocean layers without mixing substantially. The acceleration of melt rate indicates a feedback process at work.[82] Actual dynamics are perhaps more complex. This new dynamic is discussed further in Chapter 4.

Currently, this new feedback dynamic is affecting only a small portion of the Antarctic coastline. This threat could expand in two ways: (1) ice melting could ratchet to higher and higher rates, and (2) the feedback dynamic could spread along the coastline. This combination could raise sea levels much faster than currently anticipated—perhaps 10–20 times faster? More frequent and larger ice sheet collapses could also escalate the threat.

If all the ice on Antarctica were to suddenly melt, seas around the planet would rise about 65 meters (216 feet), flooding all coastlines and low-lying areas.[83] (A Greenland total melt would add about 23 feet). Although such a sudden event is considered highly unlikely, the same result is inevitable if global warming is allowed to continue unabated. Some of the glacier retreat is already considered irreversible. Even one-tenth of 216 feet would have catastrophic effects—especially during storms at high tide.

The "amplifying ice melt rates" mentioned earlier are part of a general acceleration trend in Antarctica melting. Overall, the annual melt rate from 2012 to 2017 was three times greater than between 1992 and 2011.[84] This sharp increase was confirmed by comprehensive studies funded by NASA and the European Space Agency.[85] If melting rates continue on a non-linear trajectory, then still-higher melt rates are assured. Coupled with the possibility of reaching and passing a tipping point, the prospect for catastrophic sea level rises in the foreseeable future cannot be discounted.

Recent studies are confirming that large plumes of warm, moist air, called "atmospheric rivers", are contributing to abnormally high temperatures and accelerated melting in both West and East Antarctica.[98,99] Scientists conclude these atmospheric rivers contributed to the collapse of Larson A ice shelf in 1995 and Larson B ice shelf in 2002.[99] The rivers also triggered 13 huge iceberg calving events in the first two decades of this century. March 2022 saw record-breaking temperatures, including 70 degrees above normal in the interior of East Antarctica.[98]

There is one glacier in West Antarctica that is causing near-term concerns. The rapidly retreating Thwaites Glacier's base is underwater, like those of most glaciers in West Antarctica (the top of the ice sheet is about one mile above sea level). The problem is that the glacier is retreating towards an extremely deep basin, the Bentley Subglacial Trench. Currently, Thwaites appears perched between high ground on the ocean floor and the Transantarctic mountains. As Thwaites slowly slides into the Bentley

Trench, it will allow much more ocean water to attack the ice sheet. [86] The bottom of Bentley Trench is 1.5 miles below sea level—the deepest place on continental Earth (some ocean trenches are deeper). When Thwaites reaches the bottom of Bentley Trench, the ocean could face a wall of ice 2.5 miles thick! Not only do thick ice walls calve more easily, but they release enormous icebergs.[86] By the time Thwaites retreats all the way to the Transantarctic mountains, the total ice melt from this glacier and the trench could raise all the planet's seas by 11 feet.[86] This could happen within decades, not centuries.[86]

An 11-foot sea rise could have profound effects on coastal communities, ports, and metropolitan areas. Disaster and mitigation costs would be astronomical! Little wonder that glaciologists are keeping a keen eye on the Thwaites Glacier. A joint U.S./U.K. 5-year study was launched in April 2018, involving 100 scientists from seven countries.[87]

This concludes the world tour of mountain glaciers.

Impacts of Retreating Glaciers

Two initial impacts of retreating glaciers are (1) increased stream flow due to added meltwater and (2) a growing lake in the basin being vacated by the receding glacier. The "dams" impounding the lake water are moraines of debris built up when the glacier was last advancing. These moraines are weak structures prone to giving way under increasing water pressure. Downstream debris flows, avalanches, floods and mud slides can and do occur when moraine dams fail.

The principal, long-term impacts are related to loss of fresh water sources as glaciers shrink towards extinction. Glacier stream flow typically increases during the early period of ice melting, but eventually reaches a peak flow. Continued shrinking causes melt runoff to decline[88] until the glacier is gone. There can still be meltwater from mountain snow packs, but these also shrink as rising temperatures convert places of traditional snowfall to snow/rain mix or just rainfall alone. When the glaciers and snow packs in an area are completely depleted, fresh water can no longer be stored by nature for future use. Partial loss results in reduced storage capacity—a new reality in many mountainous regions. Continued loss of glaciers results in radical changes to mountain hydrology.

Before the current climate changes, mountain glaciers and snow packs added considerable mass during cold weather periods to build up fresh water reserves. These could then maintain streamflow during warm, dry periods. Now these mountain reserves are in steady decline, and the available fresh water supply is not always sufficient when most needed. During extended droughts, those needs escalate to become dire. Such has already been the case in places like Northern India[89]; Cape Town, South Africa[90]; the Rio Grande Valley[91]; and Sao Paulo, Brazil.[90]

Fresh water for human consumption is not the only issue. Fresh water from mountain sources is also vital for hydroelectric power generation, agricultural irrigation, fisheries habitats, tourist and recreational activity, and life support for the ecosystem at large. Further, water shortages can lead to violence and international tensions.[90] Even nuclear-armed neighbors (India and Pakistan) have had water disputes and have threatened to divert water supplies from each other. As global temperatures continue to rise, so may tensions rise with depleted water supply. Population growth is another factor in increasing competition for dwindling water reserves.[90]

Recent satellite images are revealing that the world's glaciers hold less water than previously thought and fresh water supplies can be expected to peak sooner.[100] Millions of people will be impacted. Earth's 215,000 glaciers have 11% less water than former estimates. This rapid meltdown is threatening livelihoods across the planet.[100]

An Impact Profile: Skagit River Watershed

The Skagit River Watershed in northwest Washington State (USA) exemplifies impacts from shrinking glaciers. Glacial meltwater comes from the North Cascades mountain range and nearby Mt. Baker. These glaciers were briefly introduced in the world tour section above. A closer look is provided below.

Over the last 100 years, the North Cascades glaciers have lost over 50% of their surface area and Mt. Baker has lost about 30%.[92] The Skagit basin has lost 19% of glacierized area since 1959.[93] Examining five closely monitored glaciers in the North Cascades (see Figure 1-3 on the next page) it is evident glacier melting is winning the tug-of-war against snow accumulation since the late 1980s.[93] That is, mass balance has been sharply negative for all five glaciers in the last 40 years. Also, the glacier mass loss is accelerating as indicated by the steepening of curve slopes in recent years.

The combined loss of glacier volume for these five glaciers in the 50-year period between 1959 and 2009 was slightly above 3 cubic kilometers (or a layer of water 20 meters deep covering all 377 glaciers in the Skagit watershed). Another way to look at this loss of fresh water reserve is that it represents a 100-year supply for Skagit County.[93] This loss of reserve is especially critical during the dry season, when crops are in greatest need of irrigation. Fortunately, the tulips for which the Skagit Valley is famous do not require as much irrigation in the spring.

The future of glaciers in the Pacific Northwest and their capacity to support streamflow was analyzed in a recent study.[94] The study period was 1960 through 2009. One of the findings was that all studied glaciers had been declining since 1980 due to atmospheric warming. Glaciers in the Thunder Creek watershed are expected to begin rapid retreat after 2040 (its source is at a much higher altitude than many glacier-fed streams). By the year 2100, the glaciers feeding Thunder Creek are projected to cover only about 25% of the 1960 area.[94] Many other glaciers in the region could be at 10% or less of the 1960 surface area because of their lower elevation and local climate. Shrinking glaciers and snow packs could lead to streamflow reductions of up to 80% by the end of the century.[94]

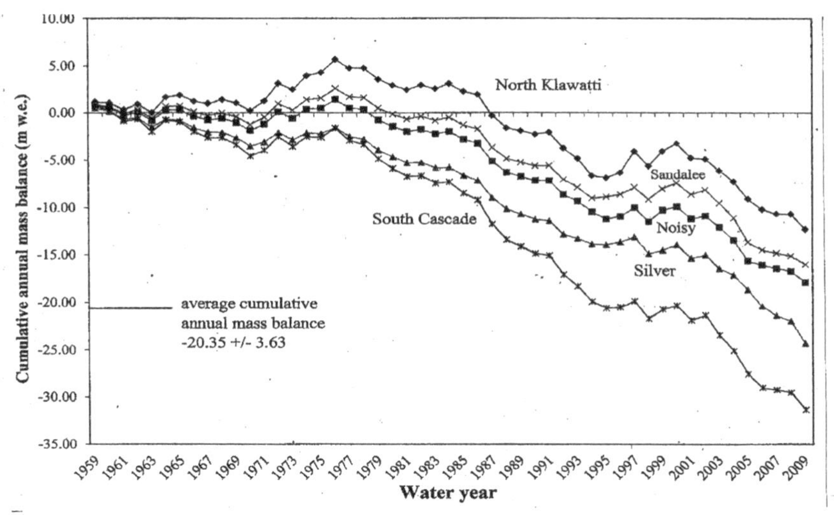

Figure 1-3 Shrinking Glaciers in North Cascades, 1959-2011

Seattle City Light is 90% dependent on hydroelectric generation: half of this from city-owned facilities and the remainder through purchases such as those from Bonneville Power Administration (which draws much of its power from dams on the Columbia River).[95] A major Seattle City Light asset is Ross Dam in the Skagit River watershed. Low streamflow in the summer can mean lost revenues from selling surplus power from city facilities, plus higher costs from Bonneville purchases.[95] Reduced streamflow during a drought in 2015 also affected support for fish habitats and recreational uses.[96] Dr. Ronda Strauch, a climate scientist at Seattle City Light, said: "We anticipate continued reductions in summer inflows (predicted from hydrologic modeling) due to warmer temperatures, reduced snowfall, and receding glaciers."[96]

Seattle City Lights' awareness of climate change impacts is not limited to generation of electricity. It anticipates that transmission and distribution will be affected by extreme weather events "such as landslides, wildfires, and floods."[97] It is preparing adaptation plans for the full spectrum of climate change impacts.

Chapter 1 Sources

1. Michael Zemp et al. "Historically unprecedented global glacier decline in the early 21st century," Journal of Glaciology published on-line, July 10, 2017 (I2348)

2. Hassan Basagic, "Twentieth Century Glacier Change in the Sierra Nevada, California," Portland State University, July 9, 2014, pp 1-3 (I2328)

3. Henry Fountain, "Warming Upheaval is Creating a 'New Arctic' a Study Report Reveals," New York Times, September 15, 2020, p. A16 (I2892)

4. Mark Fischetti, "A New Reality," Scientific American, August 2019, pp. 37-39 (I2598)

5. Patrice Taddonio, "Greenland's Glaciers are Melting Faster than Expected. See Them in 360°," PBS.org Frontline, September 20, 2018, pp. 1-4 (I2344)

6. Henry Fountain, "Soaring Temperatures Speed Up Greenland's Spring Thaw," New York Times, June 19, 2019, p. A6 (I2764)

7. Henry Fountain, "Greenland's Record Ice Loss," New York Times, August 25, 2020, p. D4 (I2882)

8. Sidney Pereira, "Puzzling Heat from Deep Inside the Earth is Melting Greenland's Glaciers," Newsweek, January 22, 2018, pp. 1-6 (I2340)

9. Jakob Abermann et al. "Mountain Glaciers -vs- Ice Sheet in Greenland," SAO/NASA, April 28, 2017. p.1. Abstract only. (I2332)

10. Staff, "Iceland's Vanishing Glaciers will Severely Affect Human Life," Iceland Magazine, May 26, 2017, pp1-3 (I2377)

11. Staff, "A Glacier's Pace," The Economist, August 8, 2020, p. 68 (I2867)

12. Staff, "Iceland Rises as its Glaciers Melt from Climate Change," PHYS.ORG, January 29, 2015, pp. 1-3 (I2375)

13. Susan Ormiston, "Dry Lakes and Dust Storms: Dramatic Changes to Yukon Glaciers are Warning for Planet, Researchers Say," CBC, October 28, 2018, pp. 1-9 (I2367).

14. Staff, "A Shortened Shelf Life," The Economist, August 15, 2020, p. 32 (I2870)

15. Staff, 'Melting of Artic Mountain Glaciers Unprecedented in Past 400 years," Science Daily (American Geophysical Union), April 10, 2018, (I2310)

16. Blaine Friedlander, "Recent Russian Artic Glacier Loss Doubles from the Previous 60 years," Cornell Chronicle, April 24, 2018, pp. 1,2 (I2362)

17. Katie Weeman, "Unprecedented Ice Loss in Russian Ice Cap," PHYS.ORG, September 9, 2018, pp 1-3 (I2361)

18. Olga Dobrovidova, "Melting Glaciers Threaten to Inundate Russia's Far North and Siberia," Science and Technology, March 24, 2017, pp. 1-4, (I2360)

19. Staff, "Norwegian Glaciers Could Melt Completely," PHYS.ORG, April 7, 2006, pp. 1–2 (I2368)

20. Hanna Hills, "Melting of Glaciers Continues," Norway Today, November 30, 2018, pp. 1, 2 (I2369)

21. Staff, "Melting of Swedish Glacier Builds Up Climate Change Fears," The Straits Times, August 4, 2018, pp 1–3 (I2370).

22. Staff, "Climate change and BC's glaciers," University of Northern BC, November 1, 2007 (I2321)

23. Staff, "Alberta Glacier Inventory and Ice Volume Estimation," Alberta Water Portal Society, November 29, 2018, pp. 1–4 (I2352)

24. N.W. Rutter, Nathan Baker, "Glaciers in Canada," The Canadian Encyclopedia, February 1, 2018, pp. 1–8 (I2354)

25. Staff, "Glaciers and Climate Change," Olympic National Park Service, December 15, 2018, p.1 (I2399)

26. Staff, "Glaciers and Climate Change," Olympic National Park Service, December 15, 2018, p. 1 (I2399)

27. Staff, "Glaciers of Washington," Portland State University, December 15, 2018, pp. 1-25 (I2398)

28. Staff, "Glaciers of Idaho," Portland State University, December 12, 2018, pp 1–6 (I2393)

29. Staff, "Glaciers Rapidly Shrinking and Disappearing: 50 years of Glacier Change in Montana," USGS, May 10, 2017, pp. 1, 2 (I2255)

30. Staff, "Time Series of Glacier Retreat," USGS, May 19. 2017 (I2260)

31. Staff, "Glaciers of Wyoming," Glaciers of the American West, July 23, 2019, pp. 1–7 (I2559)

32. Benjamin Storrow, "The Rocky Mountain's Largest Glaciers are Melting with Little Fanfare," E&E News (Scientific American), September 13, 2017, pp. 1–9 (I2558)

33. Staff, "Glaciers of Oregon," Portland State University, December 15, 2018, pp. 1–25 (I2391)

34. Staff, "Mapping Oregon's Glaciers: A Lot of Ice is Melting Away," CNN News, March 2, 2016, pp. 1–3 (I2392)

35. Staff, "Glaciers of California," Portland State University, August 24, 2011, pp. 1–8 (I2325)

36. Hassan Basagic, "Quantifying Twentieth Century Glacier Change in the Sierra Nevada, California," Portland State University (master's thesis). May 5, 2005, pp. 1–9 (I2401)

37. Staff, "Glaciers of Colorado," Portland State University, November 10, 2018, pp 1–18 (I2317)

38. Staff, "Glaciers and Climate," Rocky Mountain National Park, December 20, 2018 p.1 (I2402)

39. Bruce Finley, "Rocky Mountain Meltdown: CU scientists find Glaciers Shrinking," The Denver Post, April 18, 2016, pp. 1–3 (I2404)

40. Jacy Marmaduke, "Rocky Mountain NP Glacier Loss a Threat to Water Supply," Coloradoan, September 19, 2016, pp 1–3 (I2403)

41. Giles Tremlett, "Climate Change Lays Waste to Spain's Glaciers," The Guardian, February 23, 2009, pp 1–3 (I2364)

42. Staff, "Glacial Retreat in the Alps," NASA, LCLUC, January 11, 2007 (I2320)

43. Ilana Magra, "Giant Glacier in Alps Risks a Collapse," New York Times, September 26, 2019, p. A9 (I2771)

44. Andreas Kaab et al. "Massive Collapse of Two Glaciers in Western Tibet in 2016 After Surge-Like Instability" Nature Geoscience, February 1, 2018, pp. 114–120 (I2192)

45. Staff, "High Mountain Asia Overview," NSIDC,November 19, 2018, p.1 (I2346)

46. Miriam Nielsen, "Study: A third of Asia's Glaciers Likely Gone by 2100," Glacier-Hub, Earthsky, December 15, 2017, pp 1–5 (I2339)

47. Frank Jordans, "Study: Asia's Glaciers Face Massive Melt from Global Warming," PHYS.ORG, September 13, 2017, pp 1–2 (I2335)

48. Somini Sengupta, "Scientists Find Climate Change is 'Eating' Himalayan Glaciers" New York Times, June 20, 2019, p. A4 (I2767)

49. Staff, "Climate Science: Estimating the Fate of Asian Glaciers," Nature Asia, September 14, 2017, p.1. Abstract only. (I2336)

50. Staff, "Asia's glaciers to shrink a third by 2100, threatening water supply of millions," The Guardian, September 13, 2017, pp 1, 2 (I2333)

51. Kai Schultz, Bhadra Sharma, "Climate Crisis May Melt Most of Himalayan Glaciers by 2100," New York Times, February 15, 2019, p. A11 (I2407).

52. Bhadva Sharma, Kai Schultz, "Nepalis Forced to Flee Villages as Himalayan Climate Changes," New York Times, April 6, 2020, p. A19 (I2812)

53. Staff, "First Glaciers in Japan Recognized," The Japan Times Online April 9, 2012, p.1 (I2421)

54. Matt Williams, "Some of the Last Glaciers in the Tropics. They'll Be Gone in About a Decade," Universe Today, February 21, 2018, pp.1-9 (I2422).

55. Staff, "Humboldt's Death," The Economist, October 7, 2017, p.40 (I2120).

56. Kathryn Hansen, "Last Glacier Standing in Venezuela," NASA, August 27, 2018, pp.1-4, (I2283).

57. Carsten Braun et al., "The History and Disappearance of Glaciers in Venezuela," Journal of Latin America Geography, December 2, 2018, p.1–abstract (I2378)

58. Jacqueline de Klerk, "Columbia's Glaciers Face Extinction Within 30 Years, Claims IDEAM," TBD, August 9, 2018, pp. 1, 2 (I2381)

59. Aleszu Bajak, "Columbia's Disappearing Glaciers," LatinAmericanScience.org, July 1, 2012, pp. 1–5 (I2382)

60. Jan Rocha, "Shrinking Glaciers Cause State-of-Emergency Drought in Bolivia," The Guardian, November 28, 2016 (I2385)

61. Tim Radford, "Bolivian Glaciers Melt at Alarming Rate," Climate News Network, October 22, 2016, pp. 1–3 (I2386)

62. Gabriel Thouni, "Ecuador's Melting Glaciers ....," Erb Institute, April 3, 2018, pp. 1–4 (I2383)

63. Staff, "Ecuador Has Lost 30 Percent of its Glaciers in 30 Years Due to Climate Change, Say Scientists," Cuenca High Life, September 13, 2015, pp. 1–3 (I2384)

64. Chelsea Whyte, "Ancient Andes Glaciers Have Lost Half Their Ice in Just 40 Years," New Scientist, October 10, 2016, pp. 1–3 (I2349)

65. Jeremy Hinsdale, "Vanishing Glaciers: The Future of Water in Peru's High Andes" Columbia University Earth Institute, June 12, 2018, pp. 1-4 (I2350)

66. Nicholas Casey, "A Lifetime in Peru's Glaciers, Slowly Melting Away," New York Times, January 26, 2018, pp. 1, 6 (I2359)

67. Kathryn Hansen, "Glaciers in the Tropics, but Not for Long", NASA, December 5, 2017, pp. 1–3, (I2380)

68. Anna Lo Presti, " East African Glaciers at Risk from 'Global Drying,'" Glacier Hub, August 23, 2016, pp. 1, 2 (I2330)

69. Staff, "Africa Without Glaciers," UNEP, August 1, 2012, pp. 1–9 (I2326)

70. John Cook, "Mt. Kilimanjaro and the Global Retreat of Glaciers," Skeptical Science, October 11, 2018, p.1 (I2304)

71. Claudio Bravo, "Assessing Glacier Melt Contribution to Streamflow at Universidad Glacier, Central Andes of Chile," Hydrology and Earth Systems Sciences, July 3, 2017, pp. 1–3 (I2411)

72. F. Pelliccitti et al., "Changes of Glaciers in the Andes of Chile and Priorities for Future Work," Elsevier, December 2, 2013, pp. 1–3 (I2412)

73. David Farias-Barahona et al., "Geodetic Mass Balances and Area Changes of Echaurren Norte Glacier (Central Andes, Chile) Between 1955 and 2015," Remote Sensing, January 28, 2019, pp. 1–6 (I2413)

74. Staff, "Glaciers in Chile melt at Fastest Rate in 350 Years," BBC News, April 3, 2011, pp. 1–5 (I2387)

75. Staff, "The Impact of Glacier Retreat in the Andes," UNESCO, 1January 1, 2017, pp. 1–25 (I2351)

76. Kathryn Hansen, "Melting Beauty: The Icefields of Patagonia," NASA, March 27, 2018, pp. 1–3 (I2372)

77. Staff, "New Zealand Glaciers," NASA, NASA TV, August 6, 2017, pp. 1–3 (I2334)

78. Staff, "New Zealand's Glaciers are Shrinking," PHYS.ORG, May 19, 2018, pp. 1,2, (I2342).

79. Bethan Davies, "Antarctica," Antarctica Glaciers.org, May 11, 2018, pp. 1–12, (I2343)

80. Bethan Davies, "Glacier Changes in Antarctica," Antarctica Glaciers.org, June 22, 2017, pp. 1–8 (I2415)

81. Kendra Pierre-Louis, "Ice Shelf in Antarctica Shed a Berg Larger Than the Island of Oahu," New York Times, October 2, 2019 (I2667)

82. Chelsea Harvey, "Antarctic Glaciers are Helping Drive Their Own Melt," E&E News (Scientific American), April 20, 2018, pp. 1–8, (I2418)

83. Lee R. Kump et al., The Earth System, 3rd edition (textbook), Prentice-Hall, 2010, p.323

84. Seth Borenstein, "Antarctica's Ice Sheet is Melting 3 Times Faster Than Before," Associated Press, June 13, 2018, pp. 1–3 (I2754)

85. Earth Sciences Communications Team, "Ramp-Up in Antarctica Ice Loss Speeds Sea Level Rise," NASA, June 13, 2018, pp. 1–4 (I2755)

86. Richard B. Alley, " Is Antarctica collapsing?" Scientific American, February, 2019, pp. 40–45 (I2419)

87. Carolyn Beeler, "Just How Unstable is the Massive Thwaites Glacier? Scientists Are About to Find Out," PRI the World, May 1, 2018, pp.1–, (I2420)

88. Chelsea Harvey et al., "Shrinking Mountain Glaciers are Affecting People Downstream," Scientific American, January 23, 2018, pp. 1–6 (I2341)

89. Maria Abi-Habib et al. Temperatures and Tensions Rise as India's Water Supply Runs Low," New York Times, June 18, 2018, p. A4 (I2237.1)

90. Staff, "Thirsty Planet" (Special Report), The Economist, March 2, 2019, pp. 5–9 (I2423)

91. Henry Fountain, "Dry Year on Rio Grande Gets Dustier, with Hotter Days to Come," New York Times, May 26, 2018, pp. A1, A6 (I2222)

92. Erick Bengel, "Shrinking Glaciers: Geologist Studies Washington State's Retreating Glaciers," Daily Astorian, May 16, 2010, pp. 1–3 (I2236)

93. Jon L. Riedel, Michael A. Larrabee, "Impact of Recent Glacial Recession on Summer Streamflow in the Skagit River," Northwest Science, March 24, 2016, pp. 5-22 (I2406)

94. Chris Frans et al. "Glacier Recession and the Response of Summer Streamflow in the Pacific Northwest United States, 1960-2009," AGU 100, August 9, 2018, pp. 1–24 (I2424)

95. Crystal Raymond, "Climate Change Vulnerability Assessment and Adaptation Plan," Seattle City Light, March 28, 2019, pp. 1–12 (I2426)

96. Dr. Ronda Strauch, Climate Advisor, Seattle City Light (Private conversation), March 29, 2019, (I2427)

97. Staff, "Preparing for Climate Change," Seattle City Light, March 28, 2019, p.1 (I2425)

98. Jasen Samenow, "Ice Shelf Bigger Than NYC Shatters off Eastern Antarctic", Seattle Times, Washington Post, March 27, 2022, p. A6 (I3147)

99. Henry Fountain, "Plumes of Warm Air Caused Collapse of Antarctic Ice Shelfs in '95 and '02, Scientists Say", New York Times , April 5, 2022, p. A5 (I3156)

100. Raymond Zhong, "Glacier's Water Supply May Peak Sooner Than Expected", New York Times , February 8, 2022, p. A7 (I3134)

Chapter 2: Global Warming Evidence; Future Forecasts

Background Information

Chapter 1 established that global warming is causing a worldwide meltdown of mountain glaciers and polar ice sheets. This chapter provides further quantitative and historical proof of global warming. The cause of this warming is "greenhouse gases" in the atmosphere that absorb thermal radiation. These gases are a product of both natural processes and polluting emissions from human activity. Greenhouse gases and how they cause warming are both explained in Chapter 3.

In addition to proving global warming, Chapter 2 also examines (1) how global warming and climate change are related and (2) how greenhouse gas emissions and global warming are likely to continue increasing in the foreseeable future (especially in the absence of sufficiently effective climate action).

The general idea of worldwide global warming is that atmospheric and ocean temperatures are trending upwards from historic levels, disrupting a cooling trend that existed for centuries. Warming or cooling trends can be measured and tracked by finding how average annual global temperatures vary year to year over an extended period. Temperatures at a single location fluctuate daily and seasonally, but are averaged before being included in a global annual average.

Climatologists analyze cooling and warming trends by looking at departures from an average temperature over a long period (such as the 30-year period from 1951 through 1980). These average temperatures are called norms. Departures from these norms are called anomalies and consist of temperature differences between the norm and measured temperatures. For example, the norm (sometimes called baseline) might be the average annual surface temperature during the 20th century. Then, the global anomaly for

1 year might be, say, +0.4°F. When annual anomalies are shown along a year-to-year timeline, the general trends are easily seen. An example of these timeline charts is shown following an explanation of how local surface temperature data are transformed into a global surface average.

After daily highs and lows at a weather station are averaged, the 365-day average is computed to find the annual average for that station. The computed values for numerous weather stations around the world are the database used to determine each year's global mean surface temperature. Several adjustments are made to the data to remove unnatural distortions.

Different organizations independently compute annual global surface temperature anomalies using in-house methodologies Three such organizations are:[1.]

(1) NASA's Goddard Institute For Space Studies (GISS)

(2) NOAA's National Climate Data Center (NCDC)

(3) Joint Project of the UK Met Office Hadley Center and the University of East Anglia Climatic Research Unit (HADCRUT)

Each group uses the same temperature database, but otherwise follows independent methods for transforming these local data into estimated changes in *global* surface temperatures. This data transformation involves two important computations:

a) Adjusting local data from large metropolitan areas where solar heating and human-source heating combine to give misleading temperature measurements.

b) Converting thousands of recorded <u>single-point</u> temperature measurements into mean temperature changes for the entire global surface.

Data processing algorithms have been developed, tested, and calibrated through climate research. For example, conversion of single-point temperatures to surface-area temperatures involve interpolations and extrapolations of the single-site data. This approach yields realistic values for computing global mean surface temperature anomalies. Systemic errors are generally cancelled when temperatures are subtracted from the norm.

Global temperature averages generally stay within narrow bounds when Earth is between warming and cooling periods. However, climate changes can force temperatures outside those bounds and establish new cooling or warming trends. The beginnings and ends of ice ages are probably good examples. Ice ages begin during cooling trends and end during warming trends. Between these events, average global temperatures may fluctuate somewhat, but they remain within relatively stable bounds. Today's rapid global warming is a significant departure from natural climate changes, as explained in Chapter 3.

Besides temperature data, there are other ways to confirm warming trends. Climate warming can be detected and measured by observing the melting of glaciers and sea ice, the shrinkage of snow-covered areas, and the rise of global sea levels. Annual changes in climate can also be observed in tree rings, lakebed sediments, ice cores, and corals.[2.] These "proxy" methods can supplement and confirm computed surface temperature anomalies, though proxy measurements are considered less precise. Impacts of global warming, such as drought intensities, wildfire frequency, and heat stroke fatalities, are noteworthy statistics in substantiating warming trends.

New technology has enabled ways to measure global warming effects. Satellite technology provides precise tracking of glacier and sea ice melting, as well as snow coverage measurements. For example, the European Space Agency's CRYOSAT has measured mass loss in the West Antarctica ice shelf. NASA's GRACE system measures ice sheet losses by reductions in gravity. NASA's ICESAT accurately measures ice sheet elevations with laser sensors to determine changes in sheet thickness.[3.]

Quantitative Evidence of Global Warming and Climate Disruption

Hard evidence can now be considered to determine whether a disruptive warming trend exists. The first test is whether global surface temperatures are trending upwards. Figure 2-1 on the next page demonstrates the upward trend.[4] This NASA chart shows how the annual global temperature anomaly has varied over the 140-year period between 1880 and 2020. These anomalies are with reference to 1951–1980 mean surface temperature norm. Additional quantitative evidence in recent history is the fact the last six years are among the ten warmest since 1880.[4] Those ten warmest have all occurred

since the year 2000. The warmest year in the 140-year history was 2016, and it was nearly tied in 2020.[5] These record-breaking anomalies in recent years are among those plotted in Figure 2-1, and they indicate the unprecedented global warming is still trending upwards. The future of greenhouse gas emissions and warming is discussed later in this chapter.

Note that temperature anomaly estimates from five different organizations are shown in Figure 2-1. The original chart is in color, and color-coded lines show slight differences in anomaly estimates. Although Figure 2-1 is a black and white copy, the wobbly path of temperature versus year stays within rather narrow bounds. This remarkable agreement in results between five different in-house methods underscores the scientific credibility of this global warming evidence.

Closer inspection of Figure 2-1 reveals an increasing slope in warming trend. The 50-year period between 1880 and 1930 begins and ends at about -0.2 °C (compared to the 1951–1980 baseline). A straight "line of best fit" between 1880 and 1930 would likely be nearly parallel to a horizontal line. In other words, there was little or no significant temperature difference between the beginning and end of the 50-year period.

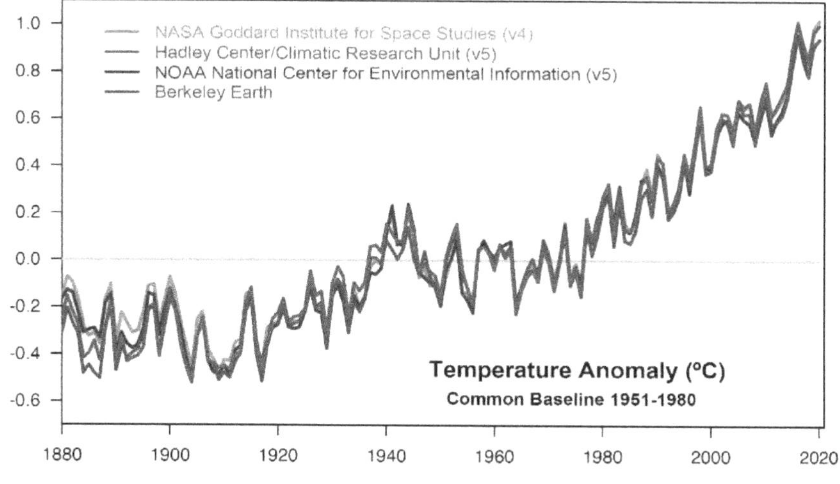

Figure 2-1 Global Temperature Anomaly

In the next 50-year period (1930-1980), the warming anomaly increases from -0.2°C to +0.1°C—a jump of approximately 0.3 °C. above the flat trend of the previous 50 years. The next 40-year period, between 1980 and 2020, shows a warming difference of about 0.8 °C. These are rough figures, but not so rough as to obscure the acceleration of global warming.

Drawing straight lines between the temperature end points of the three time periods identified above reveals a dramatic increase in line slopes, with the steepest slope in the third period (between 1980 and 2020). This means the rate of global warming is increasing sharply with time. Technical terms for this are a "non-linear" or "exponential" growth rate.

The terms "non-linear" and "exponential" are helpful to understanding the true magnitude and urgency of climate change threats. Chapter 4 provides a number of examples where climate change is being amplified by non-linear or exponential processes. One example is rapid and unstable melting of Arctic sea ice due to vicious cycles that amplify melting rates. A simple diagram in Chapter 4 illustrates the feedback process. Much of climate change is being accelerated in a like manner. A practical consequence is that future climate disasters are intensifying and arriving much sooner than if climate changes were simply linear.

The term "non-linear" is easy to explain. If global warming were a linear trend, then Figure 2-1 would be a single straight line between 1880 and 2020. But it is not. It takes at least three straight lines of differing slopes for a good approximation of the actual year-to-year global warming trend. More precise approximations of the actual warming trend would require more than three straight lines: 10, 100, or even 1,000 lines. That is because the best-fitting line is probably curved. In any case, the global warming trend is definitely non-linear (the trend cannot be reasonably described by one straight line).

The term "exponential" is also easily explained. A common term is "squared," as in the phrase "the number 3 squared equals 9." The mathematical expression is $3^2=3x3=9$. The number 2 is the exponent of the number 3. The number 3 cubed is written as $3^3=3x3x3=27$. Likewise, the number 3 with an exponent of 4 is $3^4=3x3x3x3=81$. Note that as the exponent of 3 grows from 2 to 4, the answer grows from 9 to 81. In other words, exponents are powerful amplifiers. Exponential climate change means a quickening pace of climate change and intensification of climate change impacts. These effects translate to the growing urgency of climate action.

The temperature anomaly trend illustrated in Figure 2-1 and other recent record-breaking warming facts are quantitative evidence that clearly confirms global warming. The first test of the global warming question has now been answered.

The second test of the global warming trend is hard evidence regarding glacier and sea ice melt, shrinkage of winter snow-covered areas, and rising sea levels. Evidence follows:

(1) Glaciers in all regions are losing a total of 260 billion metric tons per year[3] (Europe's CRYSAT satellite).

(2) Glaciers in Antarctica are losing 160 billion metric tons per year[3] (NASA's ICESAT)

(3) In 2015, Antarctica's sea ice area shrank 100,000 square miles (0.9%) below the 1981–2010 average.[6]

4) The annual mean Arctic ice sheet area shrank 3.5%–4.1% per decade during the 1979-2012 period.[7] March 2021 data indicate the Arctic ice sheet shrank 305,000 square miles from the 1981-2010 baseline average.[8]

(5) In December 2015, the snow cover area in the Northern Hemisphere was 190,000 square miles less than the 1981-2010 average.[6]

(6) Between 1901 and 2010, the global mean sea level rose 0.19 meters, with likelihood in the range of 0.17 meters to 0.21 meters.[7]

It must be concluded that Earth is experiencing an unprecedented warming trend (as was also demonstrated by global-wide mountain glacier melting in Chapter 1 and by Figure 2-1). **Global warming is a proven fact.** Global warming has unraveled a relatively stable climate that had prevailed up to the 19th century. Global warming also correlates with the beginning of a still-expanding industrial revolution and still-rising carbon emissions.

The Relationship Between Global Warming & Climate Change

The current global warming trend started in the early 19th century, and it is a sharp departure from the slight cooling trend during the previous 1,000 years. This new situation is continually adding heat to the environment. The net effect is a hotter atmosphere and hotter oceans (about 93% of the excess heat is absorbed by the oceans). Global warming forces changes to Earth's various climates, and the reverse is also true: global warming and climate change are interactive. One agent connecting the two is weather (as noted below).

First, the general relationship between weather and climate is discussed. Absent a new situation like global warming, the climate for a location or region (such as the tropics) varies somewhat with seasons, but otherwise the statistical pattern holds relatively constant year to year. Weather is constantly changing—sometimes slowly and sometimes quickly. In the equatorial tropics (where seasonal changes are slight), the climate holds steady decade to decade, whereas the weather often changes during each day. Afternoon showers drop surface temperatures and humidity while adding to rainfall totals.

The climate for a location or region can be described as a database of weather statistics: historical average daily high and low temperatures, record daily high and low temperatures, monthly and annual temperature statistics, precipitation statistics, etc. Weather reports in the media often compare current and predicted conditions with climate statistics.

When weather patterns change, climates change, because climate is generally defined by weather statistics. Global warming affects weather patterns because the excess heat is circulated throughout the globe by atmospheric and ocean currents. These currents move vertically (up and down) and horizontally (back and forth). For example, ocean currents carry warm equatorial water towards the poles and they return cold water towards the equator. This circulation in the North Atlantic moderates temperatures in the eastern United States and Western Europe. The excess heat from global warming alters both weather and climates in the North Atlantic region. The Arctic climate is also affected by these same ocean currents. Accelerated melting of sea ice and mountain glaciers is one result of global warming.

Atmospheric currents include the trade winds, which move air between and over continents. The jet stream is a high-velocity current in the stratosphere that has significant impact on weather across many degrees of latitude and longitude. These and other atmospheric currents distribute the excess global warming heat around the globe, affecting both weather and climates in their path.

The narrative above shows ways in which global warming affects climate change. But an earlier claim was made that climate change can also affect global warming. Two examples of this dynamic are outlined in the following paragraphs (more details are provided in Chapters 3 and 4).

In the first example, warmer oceans and a warmer atmosphere mean the water vapor evaporation rate increases at the ocean's surface. The consequence is a higher concentration of water vapor in the atmosphere. However, water vapor happens to be an important greenhouse gas that emits heat when illuminated by thermal radiation (explained in Chapter 3). When a region's climate has been changed by global warming, the elevated moisture in the atmosphere begins contributing to global warming. In this way, global warming and climate change are interactive.

In the second example, warming oceans and atmosphere have the effect of moving climate conditions towards the poles. Generally speaking, the climate that once existed at mid-latitudes is now at higher latitudes. The same general effect is at high latitudes—sub-Arctic conditions are now similar to what had existed at lower latitudes. One consequence of this climate change in the sub-Arctic is that frozen soil begins to thaw. What was permanently frozen soil (permafrost) is now in various stages of thawing during summer months.

Permafrost thawing leads to decay of organic material in the soil that was formerly frozen. Decay, in turn, causes the release of certain organic gases containing carbon into the atmosphere. These gases happen to be greenhouse gases, and like water vapor, they contribute to global warming. This situation is explained in Chapter 4. In the permafrost case, climate change and global warming are indeed interactive, and this interaction can cause the exponential amplification of changing conditions (sometimes called vicious cycle or feedback effects).

It should be noted these two examples are far from being intuitive. They involve technicalities of climate science and other sciences (such as organic chemistry). Specialists ought to be respected for their dedicated efforts to help reduce climate change risks. Science and scientists are not always appreciated, but their professional contributions are essential in combating climate change.

The Future of Global Warming and Climate Change

How long will global warming continue? That is the "64 trillion dollar" question. There is little reliable information on which to base predictions. First, pollution levels caused from human activity depend on what steps society takes towards reducing global greenhouse gases (GHG) emissions into the atmosphere. The timing and effectiveness of those steps are additional uncertainties. Finally, the scale and chemical composition of future GHG emissions are not known. For example, future demands for energy are uncertain, and the mix between clean and polluting energy generation versus time is also unknown. Also unknown are future carbon emissions from natural sources such as thawing permafrost, marine carbon reservoirs and traditional sources. The removal of carbon sinks through deforestation also adds carbon to the atmosphere. Future deforestation is another unknown.

What is known are the goals for controlling warming that have been established by national governments, meeting under the auspices of the United Nations. There is agreement, codified by the 2015 Paris Accord, on a goal to limit warming to 1.5°C above pre-industrial levels (or lower if possible). The long series of international climate negotiations up to and beyond the 2015 accord is discussed in Chapters 8 and 9. Beyond voluntary pledges to limit greenhouse emissions, the talks have not achieved consensus on an enforceable, practical plan to reduce and eliminate global GHG emissions.

So far, the cumulative sum of those climate pledges has fallen short of being able to hold global warming below the 1.5°C goal.[9] Scientists conclude GHG emissions must be cut about 50% by 2030 to avoid the most-feared climate disasters. Ms. Patricia Espinosa, head of the U.N. climate agency, observes: "current levels of climate ambition are very far from putting us on a pathway that will meet our Paris Agreement goals." [9] The last climate summit meeting between world leaders (known as COP26, held in Glasgow, Scotland in November 2021) was be another opportunity for signatories of the Paris Accord to increase their carbon emission control pledges. The next opportunity will be COP 27 to be held in Egypt.

How long will carbon pollution continue? When will temperatures stop rising and begin cooling? At what average surface temperature will global warming top out? Answers are needed to be able to predict the timing and scale of future conditions such as sea level rise, floods, wildfires, droughts, extreme storms, etc. Lacking those answers, some climate analysts might assume several arbitrary levels of peak global temperatures to cover a range of possibilities. But such arbitrary values have little practical value. Even so, arbitrary levels of 2, 4 and 8°C above pre-industrial levels have been seen in climate literature. These have been associated with the best case, moderate case, and worst case, respectively. However, the worst case (or even higher temperature) might be the best that can be achieved in the absence of effective remedies to counter climate change.

A Carbon Emissions Surge?

There are reasons to believe it would be extremely challenging to hold global warming below a worst-case scenario. Future conditions for slashing pollution emissions will probably worsen and a major surge in carbon emissions is possible.[15] There are now two major global movements underway that portend exponential increases in energy demand, with consequences of rising carbon pollution. The first is an urban population explosion[10] and the second is a new industrial revolution in developing countries.[11] India is experiencing both social shifts and could serve as a poster child for future industrial pollution. Energy needs are multiplying rapidly. China is committed to long-term dependence on coal-fired power plants, and has been promoting the same dependence in India, Africa, and much of the developing world. India is discovering the benefits of air conditioning in a hot, humid climate and can mine its own coal for generating electricity. However, it is also positioning itself for major coal imports from Australia. Ports are being expanded so that Australian coal can be brought in to India[12] India's oil and coal needs are expected to about double between 2020 and 2040, and the country will need twice as much coal as oil (in energy equivalent)[13].

India might wish to rethink their plan to support ambitious economic development with fossil fuel energy sources. The nation is now suffering from climate change impacts: An extreme heat wave is devastating North India and uninhabitable living conditions are chasing people indoors, closing schools earlier in the day and shifting scheduling in the business world.[16] Another kind of shift could help bring permanent relief: replacing carbon-based energy with hydrogen and other clean energy sources.

Africa, like India, has similar plans to power their industrial revolution with fossil fuel energy. Like India, it is currently suffering from climate change impacts: the most severe drought in four decades in the Horn of Africa (according to the World Food Programme.)[17] Africa should also consider transitioning to clean energy sources to help avoid much worse climate catastrophes in the future.

A recent study confirms that human-caused global warming is to blame for intensifying heat waves.[18]

Although coal is shunned in some industrial nations, it will likely be a prominent fuel in developing nations and could be a major contributor to a carbon emissions surge. Coal is the worst polluter of fossil fuels yet emissions from coal-fired plants jumped 17% in 2021[19] Coal is a profitable business, with Indonesia, Australia, and Russia leading the pack of coal exporters.[20] The three top consumers of coal are South Africa, China and India.[20] Twenty-seven percent of the world's energy is generated by coal-fired power plants.[20] Coal is also a cheap alternative fuel.[21]

Figure 2-2 on the next page shows the urban population explosion adding billions to Earth's metropolitan centers.[10] Expansion of those centers will require massive quantities of cement (whose production causes enormous releases of greenhouse gases). Cement manufacturing is forecasted to grow substantially, as shown in Figure 2-3 on the next page.[14]

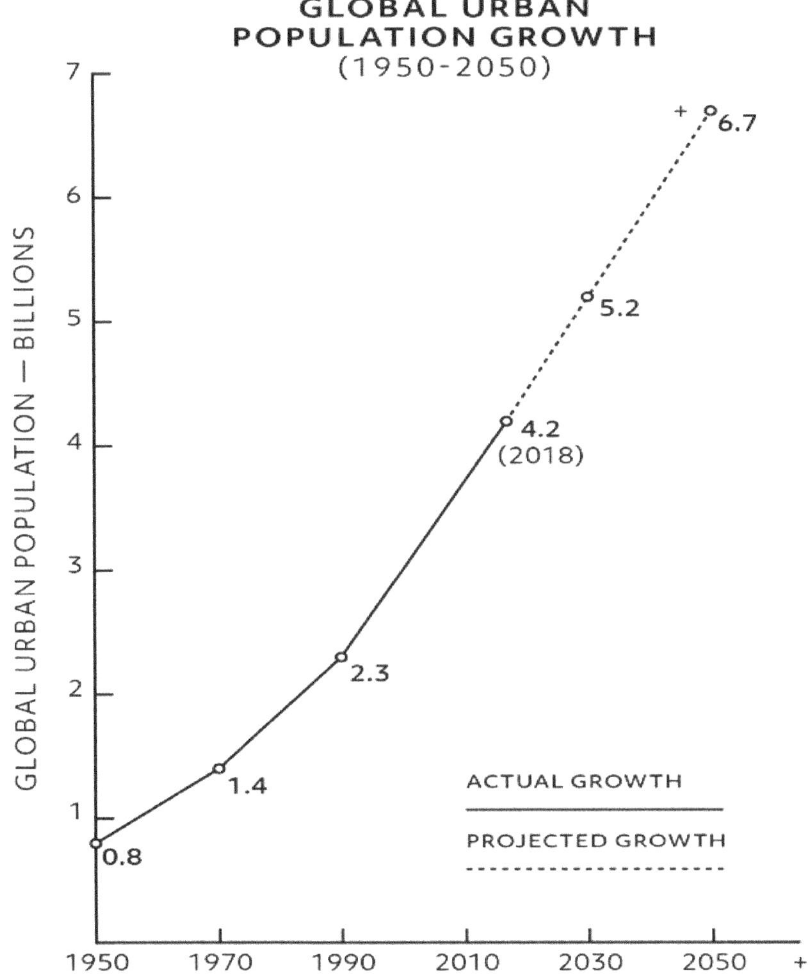

Figure 2-2 Global Urban Population Growth

The Center For Strategic and International Studies (Washington D.C.) released a report in May 2019 on the industrial revolution in the developing world.[11] This report advised: "Countries from Africa to Asia and Latin America to Eastern Europe are simultaneously urbanizing and industrializing for the first time. They are building the infrastructure for the second and third industrial revolutions."[11] Clearly, the developing world will need a great deal of cement and also expanded energy sources to power industrial plants and enlarged cities. Will those new power sources be clean or dirty? If India is any example, many of them will be burning coal—a "worst case" polluting fuel.

The double whammy of urban population explosion and new industrial revolutions virtually assures an emissions surge if the current dependency on fossil fuels continues.

There are signs the carbon emissions surge is already underway. Global methane emissions hit a new record in 2021 following the largest one-year increase in four decades.[22] According to the National Oceanic and Atmospheric Administration (NOAA) the methane level in the atmosphere is now 250% greater than before the Industrial Revolution.[22] The European satellite Sentinel 5 discovered "ultra emitters" among the methane sources. These giant leaks were clearly identified with petroleum activity in the United States, Russia and Central Asia.[23]

In addition to methane setting a new record, carbon dioxide set a new record in 2022.[24] NOAA reports the CO_2 concentration in the atmosphere is now the highest it has been in the last four million years![24] This is more evidence the carbon emissions surge has already started.

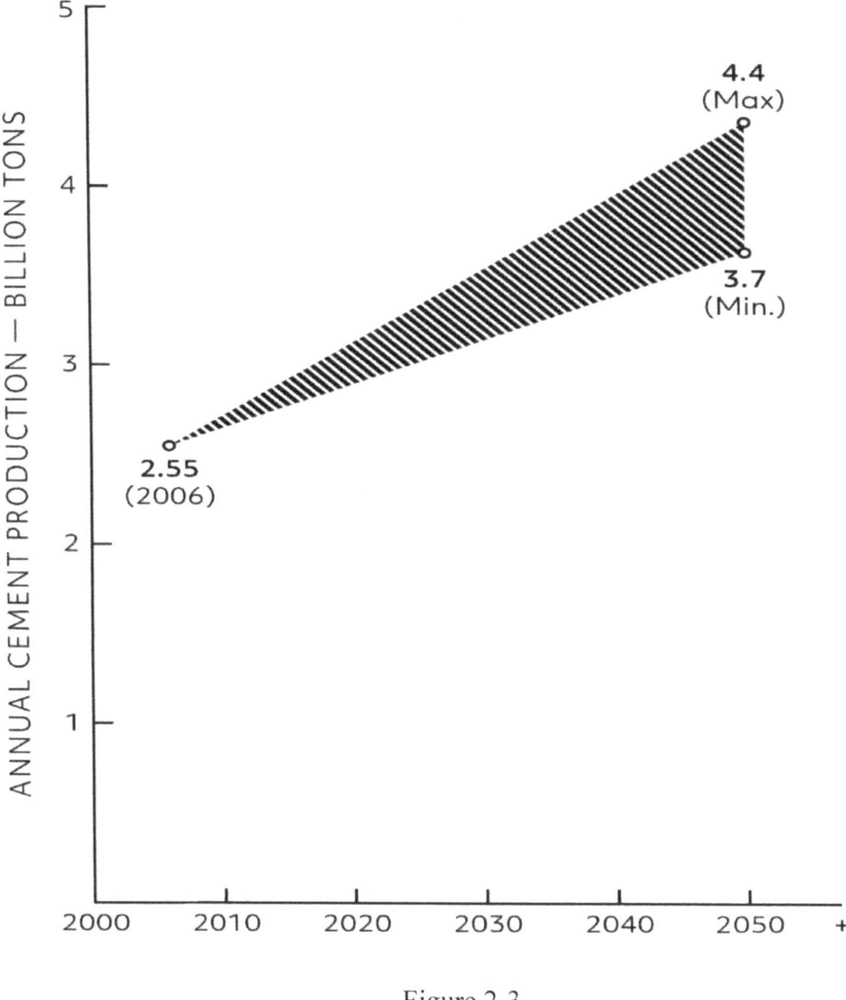

Figure 2-3

Rick Spinard, NOAA administrator, remarked this new emissions record is "a stark reminder that we need to take urgent, serious steps to become a more climate-ready nation" [24]

A second sign of increasing carbon emissions is that from thawing permafrost in the Arctic.[25] As the soil warms, decaying organic material releases greenhouse gases (explained in Chapter 4). Methane is also highly explosive as was demonstrated by a NOVA TV program showing huge sinkholes in the Arctic permafrost.[26] The Arctic is warming at twice the rate as elsewhere.[27] A recently published study estimates the top three meters of permafrost could release 624 million tons of carbon *per year* by 2100.[25]

Further evidence of changing conditions that are consistent with a carbon emissions surge is the rapid increase in losses of carbon sinks in the Amazon forest. The recent pace of deforestation is the highest in 15 years.[28] Over 5,000 square miles of forest were lost between August 2020 and July 2021.[28] The semi-controlled fires that cleared land (primarily for agriculture and mining) produced 2.5 billion metric tons of polluting carbon dioxide.[29] Deforestation hits the climate in two ways: (1) Immediate greenhouse gas pollution from burning carbon and (2) removal of carbon sinks for generations. Near-term prospects for ending tropical rainforest deforestation are unclear at best (explained in Chapter 7).

The possibility of a carbon emissions surge becomes a probability if society continues to pursue net-zero emissions by 2050 or later. An authority on the situation thinks the surge is certain if rich countries don't help less-developed nations with near-term transition to clean energy.[15] India's goal is net-zero emissions by 2070. Others, such as Indonesia and Saudi Arabia, have committed to 2060.[15] The surge would become virtually assured if society continues to depend on fossil fuel for the indefinite future. In other words, the surge is highly probable if society fails to adopt the Chapter 11 climate action proposals or some other aggressive action plan of similar scale and urgency. The carbon emissions surge might be subject to mitigation if society changes course. Currently, that is a big if.

The focus of Chapter 11 is on solutions to the climate crisis. Chapter 11 outlines important ingredients of an effective climate action plan. One objective of the chapter is to establish reasons for optimism.

Chapter 2 Sources

I. James Hansen, "Global Surface Temperature Change," Reviews of Geophysics, December 14, 2010 (I1655)

2. Michael Mann et al., "Northern Hemisphere Temperatures During the Past Millennium," Geophysical Research Letters, March 15, 1999, pp. 759-762 (I1654)

3. Staff, "The Big Melt Accelerates," New York Times, May 20, 2014, p. D1 (I1433)

4. Earth Science Communications Team (JPL), "Why Does the Temperature Record Shown on Your 'Vital Signs' Begin at 1880?" NASA, April 29, 2021, pp. 1-3 (I3060)

5. Henry Fountain, "Global Analysis of Weather puts 2020 in a Tie With 2016 as the Hottest Year on Record," New York Times, January 9, 2021, p. A8 (I2966)

6. Staff, "Global Summary Information," NOAA, December, 2015 (I1658)

7. Staff, "Climate Change 2014," Intergovernmental Panel on Climate Change (IPCC) (I1656)

8. Staff, "The Dark Winter Ends," National Snow and Ice Data Center (NSIDC), April 6, 2021, pp. 1– 4 (I3054)

9. Somini Sengupta, "New Targets for Emissions Fall Far Short of Paris Goals," New York Times, February 27, 2021, p. A9 (I3022)

10. Department of Economic and Social Affairs, "World Urbanization Prospects," United Nations, January, 2019, pp. 1-126 (I2670)

11. Romina Bandura, et al., "Beyond Technology: The Forth Industrial Revolution in the Developing World," Center for Strategic & International Studies (CSIS), May, 2019, pp. 1–13 (I2669)

12. Somini Sengupta, "In an Australian Project, a Second Life for Coal," New York Times, August 16, 2019, pp. 1, 18 (I2621)

13. OPEC Secretariat, "World Oil Outlook 2017," IBBN1978-3-9503936-4-4 October, 2017, Table 2.7 (I2668)

14. Madeline Rubenstein, "Emissions From the Cement Industry," Columbia University Earth Institute, May 9, 2012, pp. 1-3 (I2607)

15. Kelly Sims Gallagher, "The Coming Carbon Tsunami", Foreign Affairs, January/February, 2022, pp. 151-164 (I3125)

16. German Lopez, "Unequal Toll From Climate Change's Effects", New York Times , June 4, 2022, p. A8 (I3170)

17. Staff, "Survival of the Bookish", The Economist, June 4, 2022, pp, 52-54 (I3171)

18. Henry Fountain, "Warming of Planet is Fueling Heat Waves", New York Times , May 24, 2022, p. A4 (I3168)

19. Brad Plumer, "Coal Use and Traffic Erase Covid Decline",New York Times , January 10, 2022, P. A11 (I3126)

20. Staff, "Soot, Loot, Reboot", The Economist, January 23, 2022, pp. 43-44 (I3128)

21. Staff, "Glencove's Message to the Planet (Coal is Alive and Kicking)", The Economist, January 1, 2022, p. 52 (I3124)

22. Raymond Zhong, "Methane Emissions, Noxious to Climate, Soared to Record in 2021, Scientists Say", New York Times, April 8, 2022, p. A17 (I3151)

23. Henry Fountain, "European Satellite Detects Huge Methane Leaks in the U.S., Russia and Elsewhere", New York Times, February 5, 2022, p. A10 (I3132)

24. Henry Fountain, "Carbon Dioxide Levels in Atmosphere Reach 4 Million-Year High and Continue to Climb", New York Times, June 4, 2022, p. A9 (I3174)

25. Staff, "Unfrozen North", The Economist, January 15, 2022, pp. 68-69 (I3127)

26. Staff, "NOVA: Arctic Sinkholes", KCTS 9 (PBS) Viewer Guide, February 2022, p. 5 (I3130)

27. Raymond Zhong, "Climate Report on the Arctic Has a Warning for Warmer Places", New York Times , December 15, 2021, P. A8 (I3122)

28. Manuela Andreoni, "Deforestation of Amazon Skyrockets to a 15-Year High", New York Times , November 20, 2021, p. A4 (I3120)

29. Henry Fountain, "9.3 Million Acres of Old Tropical Forests Lost", New York Times , April 29, 2022, p. A8 (I3161)

Chapter 3: Global Warming Causes & the Greenhouse Effect

Is the globe is really warming? The answer is "yes." This was proven in the previous two chapters, with supporting quantitative evidence. Global warming is not a hoax, as some have suggested. The current warming trend is a sharp departure from the climate that had prevailed for some 1,000 years. What is causing this anomaly? Is it simply a result of natural processes, or do human activities have some role? What is the science of atmospheric warming? What is meant by "greenhouse effect"? These are questions addressed in this chapter.

Natural Causes of Atmospheric Warming

The Earth's atmosphere is continuously warmed and cooled as the planet rotates on its axis and as it makes its annual trek along its orbit around the Sun. Exactly how the atmosphere is warmed by greenhouse gases is not so difficult to understand for readers with a science background, but some basic concepts could be challenging for others. A short "chemistry lesson" is provided here:

What do rocks, reptiles and rivers have in common with hats, heart valves, and handbags? They all consist of atoms and molecules—basic building blocks of every material substance. Molecules are built from atoms. Pure water, for example, is a molecule made up of three atoms bonded together: two hydrogen (H) atoms and one oxygen (O) atom. The chemical notation for water is simply H_2O—a familiar fact.

A water molecule is H_2O whether the water is frozen solid into ice, in liquid form or evaporated into a gas (water vapor in the atmosphere). Water vapor is also an important greenhouse gas in the atmosphere. This concludes the chemistry lesson.

Earth's climate in its natural state is a relatively comfortable habitat for human occupation (starkly different from outer space). One reason it is comfortable is that nature has provided a way for Earth's environment to be gently warmed by thermal radiation resulting from chemical processes in air molecules. It has also provided a "thermostat" to keep temperatures in a mostly comfortable range. This "thermostat" is a natural balance between elements that control weather.

The Greenhouse Effect

Nature's scheme for heating Earth's environment is the "greenhouse effect," in which certain gases in the atmosphere absorb and re-emit thermal radiation. When greenhouse gas molecules absorb thermal radiation it increases their kinetic energy by way of increased vibration amplitudes or rotation rates. This is what causes mercury to expand in a thermometer and move up the graduated scale. Temperature is defined by a molecule's kinetic energy (kinetic means moving).

Greenhouse gas molecules can be thought of as little heaters (they multiply when pollution emissions enter the atmosphere). Only greenhouse gases have the right molecules to be engaged in the process described above. These little heaters also have at least three atoms bonded together. Atmospheric nitrogen and oxygen molecules, for example, have only two atoms each, and do not qualify as greenhouse gases. The most important gases that do qualify are water vapor (H_2O), carbon dioxide (CO_2), and methane (CH_4). Other greenhouse gases have minor concentrations in the atmosphere.

The ability of greenhouse gases to absorb and radiate thermal energy is confined by the window(s) of electromagnetic wavelengths in which they function. For example, water vapor has three wavelength windows, at 1–3, 5–8, and 15–50 micrometers.[1] (One micrometer is one-millionth of a meter.) Carbon dioxide, by contrast, has two narrow windows at 3–5 and 15 micrometers, and is therefore much more constrained than water vapor. This fact plays into the argument about which gas is the most important contributor to the greenhouse effect.

Natural Surface Temperatures

Natural temperature fluctuations are affected by clouds passing overhead, air pressure variations that drive surface and higher-altitude winds, and by ocean currents that transport cool or warm water over long distances. Despite all these natural fluctuations, the average annual temperature across the globe's surface remains fairly constant from year to year. Even so, there are natural events like large lightning-caused wildfires and volcanic ash eruptions that can temporarily disrupt average temperatures.

The process climatologists use to determine average annual global surface temperature is discussed in Chapter 2. Natural forces can cause average temperatures to drift somewhat over long periods. Viewing year-to-year average temperatures over a short interval, say 20 years, would not likely reveal such a drift. A 1,000-year interval might show a slight trend. Indeed, a 1999 study showed a slight cooling trend between 1000 AD and 1850 AD.[2] That same study also revealed a sharp warming turnaround beginning about 1850 (See Figure 2-1 in Chapter 2). That climate anomaly continues to the present day, and was confirmed by the Hansen et al.'s study,[3] discussed in Chapter 2. There is no evidence this disruption was triggered by natural events or processes.

Unnatural Causes of Climate Change

What is the unnatural situation causing global warming? The consensus of some 2000 scientists on the Intergovernmental Panel on Climate Change (IPCC) is as follows:[4]

"Anthropogenic (human caused) greenhouse gas emissions have increased since the pre-industrial era driven largely by economic and population growth. From 2000 to 2010 emissions were the highest in history. Historical emissions have driven atmospheric concentrations of carbon dioxide, methane, and nitrous oxide to levels that are unprecedented in at least the last 800,000 years, leading to an uptake of energy by the climate system."

This means human activity polluting the atmosphere is to blame for much higher atmospheric concentrations of greenhouse gases that convert thermal radiation to more energetic air molecules (warmer air). The greenhouse effect is a natural process that, under normal greenhouse gas concentrations, makes Earth more comfortable for human habitation. Growing air pollution due to increased human activity has caused the upward trend in global temperatures.

Today, there is an unnatural and growing level of greenhouse effect in Earth's atmosphere. That level will likely return towards normal when humanity learns how to greatly reduce air pollution. Pollution sources include emissions from power plants, industrial plants, cargo ships, cruise ships, passenger aircraft, cargo aircraft, locomotives, automobiles, trucks, farm equipment, construction equipment, etc. Clean energy technology offers considerable promise for reducing polluting emissions of greenhouse gases, as explained in Chapter 11.

General Effects of Global Warming

Weather records are frequently being broken by global warming. The monumental devastation caused by Hurricanes Katrina and Sandy is an example of unprecedented events in the last 200 years. Many climatologists believe we are in a "new ballgame" in which climate disasters are intensifying and becoming more common. Impacts of global warming (such as accelerated thawing of glaciers and sea ice) are sometimes difficult to predict. Observed rates of melting have sometimes exceeded predictions. Still, much is being learned from the observed effects of global warming. The next four chapters provide numerous examples of how global warming is affecting climate change. The resulting climate threats and disasters are delineated.

Chapter 3 Sources

1. Lee R. Kump et al. The Earth System 3rd edition, Prentice Hall, 2010, pp. 1–420

2. Michael Mann, et al., "Northern Hemisphere Temperatures During the Past Millennium," Geophysical Research Letters, March 15, 1999, pp. 759–762 (I1654)

3. James Hansen, et al., "Global Surface Temperature Change," Reviews of Geophysics, December 14, 2010, pp.1–29 (I1655)

4. Staff, "Climate Change 2014," Intergovernmental Panel on Climate Change (IPCC) (I1656)

Chapter 4: Unstable Climate Dynamics: Roots of Risk

This chapter on unstable climate dynamics should help in understanding why climate change is an urgent threat. Tornadoes are an example of atmospheric dynamics in which wind speed and direction are changing violently in the space of seconds and yards. In the dynamics of global warming, the average surface temperature over the Earth is rising a few degrees over a 100-year period. Tornadoes are understandably dangerous. Why is global warming dangerous? One answer is that this gradual warming trend can enable unstable dynamics that lead to quickly changing and dangerous conditions. Another answer is that climate dynamics can be non-linear or exponential, as explained in Chapter 2. A longer answer is expressed by the nine stories that follow.

Global Warming Avalanches

This is an example of a catastrophic dynamic that has no known historical precedent—it appears to be entirely new to the global warming era. A unique kind of glacier instability occurred in 2002 when the lower portion of the Kolka Glacier (Caucasus Mountains) suddenly detached from the upper glacier.[1.] This glacier detachment sent an extremely massive avalanche hurtling down the valley at high speeds, killing 120 victims. Unprecedented were (1) this type of glacier instability and (2) the extreme momentum of the avalanche for a low-angle (moderate grade) valley glacier.

This glacier collapse and resulting avalanche were at first considered to be a singular, freak event.[1] However, in 2016, two more such events occurred in a remote area of the Tibetan Plateau.[1] The snow and ice contained in each of these two avalanches could fill 1 million freight train cars stretching 7,500 miles.[2] The extensive area damaged by these massive avalanches is visible from space. At top speeds, these avalanches reached 300 kilometers per hour (186 mph).[2] Scientific analyses of these avalanches concluded they were caused by "climate and weather" factors.[1] Glacier surfaces had been heavily crevassed, and extreme rainfalls in recent years had contributed to reducing friction at the glacier's base.[1] These catastrophic events raise questions of potential risks to populated areas located beneath such low-gradient valley glaciers.

Again, these catastrophic events have no known historical precedent. They are further evidence of global warming/climate change that enable this new type of glacier instability and massive avalanches.

Vicious Cycle and Melting Arctic Ice

Another example of an unstable dynamic caused by global warming/climate change is the rapid melting of Arctic sea ice in recent decades. The cause of accelerated melting is a vicious cycle described here and illustrated in Figure 4-1 (on the next page). This diagram should be read counter-clockwise, beginning with the top box labeled "INCREASING ARCTIC OCEAN & AIR TEMPERATURES (GLOBAL WARMING"). Downward and to the left are two boxes, labeled "SHORTER ICE ACCUMULATION SEASON - LONGER MELT SEASON" and "FASTER ICE MELT RATE." Each of these is a consequence of warmer temperatures (top box). Down and to the right is a single box labeled "EXPANDING HOLES IN SEA ICE," which is a consequence of the two prior boxes. Upwards to the right is a single box labeled "INCREASED SOLAR HEATING OF OCEAN," again a consequence of the prior box.

Finally, there is a return to the top box. The vicious cycle has completed one complete loop in this narrative.

Figure 4-1. Vicious Cycle Melting of Arctic Sea Ice

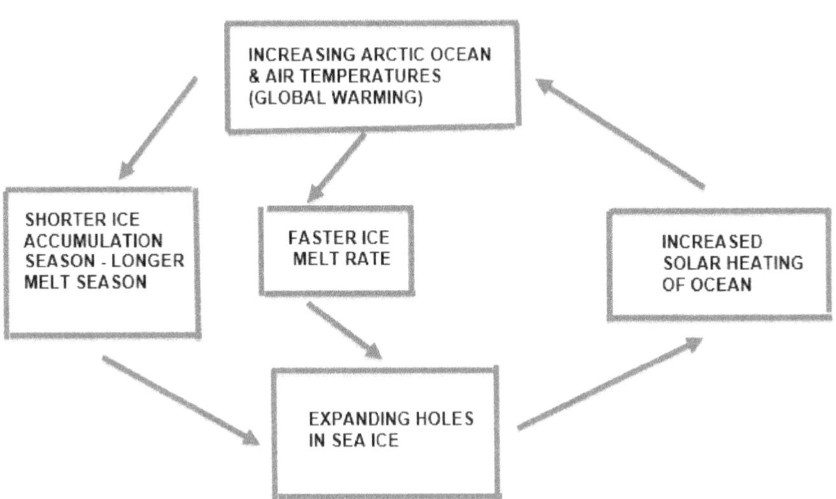

With this understanding of how to read the figure, the logical sequence of events can be appreciated. The expanding holes in the ice open more ocean surface to direct penetration by sunlight (in addition to reducing ice surfaces that reflect sunlight to the sky), thereby raising ocean temperatures. The now-higher ocean temperatures accelerate sea ice melting, causing an even higher rate of ice-free area expansion.

This narrative of the vicious cycle (sometimes called "circle") has completed the first full cycle, but it does not stop there. It goes around a second time, leaving behind a still faster ice melt rate, bigger holes in the ice, etc. Then it goes around a third, fourth, fifth, hundredth, or thousandth time, etc., each time leaving behind another boost in the boxed quantities. The cycle is considered vicious because it spins out of control and continues to gain strength. The self-amplification of the melt rate cannot be stopped until (1) all the ice has melted or (2) global warming has reversed to global cooling.

This vicious cycle effect in Arctic ice sheet melting is widely acknowledged.[3,4,5] Satellite measurements of sea ice loss are provided in Chapter 2, and these prove accelerated melting in the Arctic. Cruise ships have been seen near Pt. Barrow, Alaska in areas newly freed from ice. Indigenous communities are being forced to relocate because thinning ice has devastated their habitats. They join the ranks of other climate refugees dislodged by climate change.

Sudden Warming in the Antarctic

Until recently, most of the dynamic climate changes in Antarctica have been in West Antarctica, while the largely unexplored East Antarctica has appeared relatively stable. Now, there is a new dynamic that affects both West and East coastlines, and it is amplifying ice melt rates.[6] The "Before" and 'Now" illustrations in Figure 4-2 (on the next page) help explain the new warming dynamic. Some specifics of the illustration are this author's interpretation of the observational evidence. A more complete understanding of these dynamics will likely require additional observations and analysis.

The new reality is that warm ocean water now penetrates further towards the coastline, under ice sheets and shelves and nearer to the face of glaciers. Before, the ocean water was chilled by "pre-mixing" with ice-melt runoff. Now, the incoming warm currents slide under stratified ocean layers without mixing substantially. The acceleration of the melt rate indicates a feedback process at work.[6,7] Actual dynamics are likely more complex than those illustrated in Figure 4-2.

Currently this new feedback dynamic is affecting only a small fraction of the Antarctic coastline. This threat could expand in two ways: (1) ice melting could ratchet to higher and higher rates, and (2) the new feedback dynamic could spread along the coastline. This combination could raise sea levels much faster than currently anticipated.

Figure 4-2. Sudden Warming: Antarctic Accelerated Ice Melt

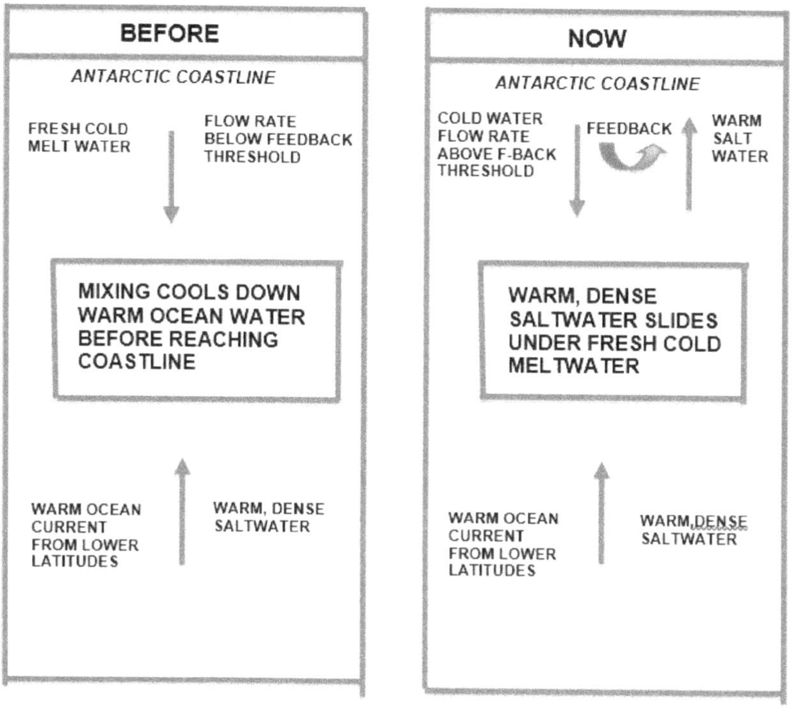

BEFORE

ANTARCTIC COASTLINE

FRESH COLD MELT WATER

FLOW RATE BELOW FEEDBACK THRESHOLD

MIXING COOLS DOWN WARM OCEAN WATER BEFORE REACHING COASTLINE

WARM OCEAN CURRENT FROM LOWER LATITUDES

WARM, DENSE SALTWATER

NOW

ANTARCTIC COASTLINE

COLD WATER FLOW RATE ABOVE F-BACK THRESHOLD

FEEDBACK

WARM SALT WATER

WARM, DENSE SALTWATER SLIDES UNDER FRESH COLD MELTWATER

WARM OCEAN CURRENT FROM LOWER LATITUDES

WARM,DENSE SALTWATER

More frequent and larger ice sheet/shelf collapses could also quicken the threat of rising seas because these collapses ultimately speed the rate at which glaciers break off into the sea.

Vicious Cycle Quickens Thawing of Permafrost

A unique consequence of global warming is large-scale thawing of permafrost (frozen soil). This, in turn, contributes to additional greenhouse warming, resulting in a vicious cycle. When permafrost thaws, the unfrozen soil begins to decompose as microbes consume the unfrozen plant and animal remains. That decomposing process results in CO_2 and methane gas emissions, adding to the abnormally high level of greenhouse effect in the atmosphere.[9]

The permafrost vicious cycle is illustrated in Figure 4-3 (on the next page). As noted earlier, a “vicious circle” or "vicious cycle" situation continues to gain strength until something disrupts it. A reversal of global warming is potentially one such event.

Studies are being made to determine the current level of thawed permafrost emissions and to predict the rate of increased emissions.[9] Sensor data indicate 5% to 15% of the carbon locked up in permafrost could escape in this century. A 10% release could amount to 130–160 billion metric tons.[9] Questions abound as to how much actual release to expect. Permafrost covers about 6 million square miles of Earth's surface. A new study of thawing rates, using different assumptions, predicts a 20% faster rate than previously thought.[10] The thawing permafrost is already causing problems with roads and building foundations on the North Slope of Alaska, in the Yukon, and in parts of Siberia.[10] Making matters worse, northward-migrating beavers are accelerating permafrost thawing by damming rivers and streams.[11]

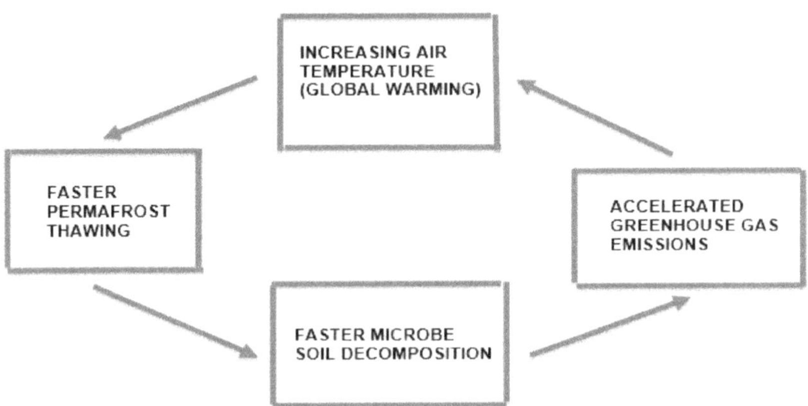

Figure 4-3. Vicious Cycle: Accelerated Permafrost Thawing

Climate Change Modifies Ocean and Atmospheric Currents (and vice versa)

This example of global warming dynamics has to do with profound changes to ocean currents, atmospheric currents, and sea ice. It also underlines the complexity and uncertainty that challenges a complete understanding of global warming and its effects.

Some clarification is needed regarding natural climate dynamics versus dynamics modified by global warming. The "thawing permafrost" dynamic discussed earlier is an example of a large-scale dynamic that has not existed in recent history. It is a new dynamic triggered by global warming. Some might say that dynamic is composed of natural processes, such as decomposition of thawed soil by microbes. While true, the large-scale vicious circle dynamic post-dates the onset of global warming. It is abnormal or unnatural compared to the natural climate dynamics that existed before global warming.

Before global warming, Earth's atmosphere and oceans had a number of natural dynamics, such as the jet stream in the upper atmosphere and the Gulf Stream current in the Atlantic Ocean (discussed later). The advent of global warming is coincident with dramatic changes in the atmospheric jet stream, ocean Gulf Stream and other natural dynamics. The newly modified dynamics are even less fully understood than the unmodified ones were. In many cases, it is still possible to determine whether global warming is a direct cause of climate change impacts. Considerable progress in rigorous attribution science has been made in the last decade, as discussed in Chapter 5.

The atmospheric jet stream, the Gulf Stream current in the Atlantic Ocean, and sea ice/glacier melting are examples of climate dynamics undergoing profound changes in recent decades. Before global warming, the jet stream changed trajectories rather predictably with the seasons. The oscillation of ridges and troughs moved across continents at "normal" speed, and the shapes of ridges and troughs followed familiar patterns. Much of that has now changed. The pattern occasionally has much deeper troughs and much higher ridges, allowing extreme weather events in the far north, the deep south, and in between.[12.] The west-east cross-continent speed of the jet stream can stall out at times, causing prolonged droughts or excessive precipitation over large areas. It is also believed the melting glaciers and sea ice in the Arctic have a role in disrupting the jet stream.[12.]

The Gulf Stream, which transports tropical waters toward the North Atlantic, has weakened and slowed. This weather-making ocean current is joined by other major currents (such as the North Equatorial current, the Labrador current, and the Greenland currents) to form a "conveyor belt" dynamic that delivers warm surface water to the far north and returns cool, deep water to the sub-tropics. Normally, this circulation provides a moderate climate to northeast North America and Western Europe. This "conveyor belt," called the Atlantic Meridional Overturning Circulation (AMOC), slowed down by one-third from mid-2009 to mid-2010, perhaps causing abnormally cold winters in the U.K. and Western Europe.[13] Year-to-year variations in AMOC strength have reached 70%, depending on wind and seawater temperature.[13] The dynamics behind the AMOC are not fully understood, but many climatologists suspect the melting sea ice (especially in Greenland) is causing its slowdown. Fresh water from the ice melt dilutes the Atlantic's saltwater, making surface water less dense. This may explain why the north end of the AMOC is allowing less of the ocean current to sink and return south.[14] Some climatologists are skeptical but, in any event, the situation is fraught with uncertainties. Sensor data in the North Atlantic are becoming more available, but there is no guarantee these data will explain the new AMOC dynamic.

Climatologists fear the AMOC might come to a complete stop, as they believe has happened in the distant past. Such an event would plunge the North Atlantic and adjoining continents into a deep freeze.[14]

Sea-ice loss in the Atlantic was noted in Chapter 2, and some of the dynamics were explained above. Worrisome features include the accelerating melt rate and the loss of ice shelves (which help keep glaciers from sliding catastrophically into the ocean).

Pathogens Thrive on Global Warmth

Another example of how global warming enables new dynamics is the blooming of previously unknown bacteria, viruses, and fungi in the warmer ocean.[15] These pathogens, in turn, are killing marine life and threatening human health. First, it should be observed that over 90% of the excess heat retained by the planet since 1955 is stored in the oceans.[16] Much of that excess is stored between depths of 300 meters and 1,500 meters, but the remainder warms ocean surface layers.[17.]

The interaction of polluted oceans and warmer water is causing the pathogen blooms noted above. A study of Florida's coastal region has traced the migration of pathogens from some 1.6 million septic tanks into coastal waters.[15] Human activities such as swimming, windsurfing and boating in the polluted waters are responsible for widespread infections. One study found one-quarter of beach users developed eye, ear, and throat infections, or respiratory and gastrointestinal disease. Some viruses found in the polluted water have been linked to diabetes, heart disease, hepatitis, and meningitis.[15] About 1% of users became chronically infected.

Damage to coral life is a well-known result of global warming.[15] One reef along the Florida coast had a 62% death rate. An ocean studies specialist at the University of Georgia noted that these killing pathogens "are new to science."[15]

A Greener Planet

Not all the new dynamic interactions enabled by global warming are making matters worse. One is actually helping to reduce carbon dioxide concentrations in the atmosphere. Atmospheric warming in the high latitudes is allowing plant growth where it was formerly too cold. The planet has turned greener in an area about twice the size of the United States.[18.] This plant growth is good news because photosynthesis removes CO_2 from the air (with the help of sunlight and water). Also, high CO_2 concentrations actually increase plant absorption rates.

This "greening dynamic" is probably behind the slowing of CO_2 concentrations in recent years. Since 2002, CO_2 concentrations in the atmosphere have risen only slightly, despite the continuing high rate of human-caused pollution.[18.] This benefit from planet greening may be nearly exhausted, however. There is a counter dynamic. In areas where snow and ice had previously reflected sunlight, new green areas now absorb sunlight and then release greenhouse gases like methane. So it is with global warming dynamics. The interactions can be subtle and complex.

Global Warming and Extreme Flooding

As the environment continues to warm, extreme weather events are becoming more frequent and intense. The basic reason is simple: more heat means more energy to fuel the storms. But the atmospheric dynamics behind extreme weather are far from simple. Fortunately, the June 2019 issue of Scientific American carried an insightful article to help dispel the complexity. Authored by Dr. Jennifer Francis, a senior climate scientist at Woods Hole Research Center (Falmouth, MA), this article is titled "Rough Weather Ahead."[19] One thing that makes the weather rough is the high costs to survive and recover from the disasters. In 2018, extreme weather caused $160 billion in worldwide losses.[19]

The bulk of the extreme weather costs are attributed to flooding disasters. What is behind such extreme flooding? Dr. Francis explains it is due to "the global effect of more heat in the ocean and more heat and (water) vapor in the atmosphere." She elaborates by pointing out water vapor is a greenhouse gas "that traps heat (and) it releases even more heat when it condenses into clouds."[19] Flooding events are gaining greater notice because of their greater frequency and disastrous impacts. Dr. Deke Arndt, a climate scientist at the National Oceanic and Atmospheric Administration (NOAA), has explained that heavy precipitation and flooding "is an expected and observed consequence of climate change."[20] The NOAA forecasted that some 25 states could expect "major or moderate flooding" between March and May 2019.[21]

Massive flooding is not the only extreme weather that is increasing. Category 4 and 5 hurricanes have been multiplying in recent decades. Between 1990 and 2010, there were 5 years in which there were at least 4 hurricanes of that strength. In the previous 4 decades, there was only 1 year that had at least 4 hurricanes of that strength, according to a chart published by the National Hurricane Center.[22] Hurricanes are becoming stronger, producing more rain, building intensity quicker, and making landfall at higher latitudes.[29] According to a recent study, they are also showing greater endurance after landfall.[30]

Hurricanes Harvey, Irma, and Maria contributed to U.S. extreme weather losses totaling $306 billion in 2017.[23] According to a recent study published in Nature Climate Change, such simultaneous, multiple climate disasters are expected to increase.[24] By the year 2100, as many as six climate disasters could strike at the same time, causing such problems as "heat waves, wildfires, sea level rise, hurricanes, flooding, drought, and shortages of clean water." [24]

Future climate threats are not just a matter of how many crises strike at any given time, but also the intensity of extreme weather events. Heat and water vapor play a role in the latter. As mentioned above, most of the excess heat produced by global warming is stored in the oceans. A chart published by The Economist in its September 22, 2018 issue illustrates a steady rise in ocean temperatures since the 1950s.[25] Prior to Hurricane Harvey making landfall in August 2017, waters in the Gulf of Mexico were at a peak temperature. After the disastrous flooding of Houston and surrounding area, analyses showed the drop in the Gulf waters' heat content matched the rainfall released by Harvey.[25.]

Extreme flooding of the Houston area was caused, in part, by the extreme water vapor/clouds and air temperatures that fueled Harvey. Another principal cause was the fact that Harvey stalled after making landfall (similar to the Hurricane Dorian stall over the Bahamas). Jennifer Francis (cited earlier) commented on the Dorian stall: "[T]his is yet another example of the kind of slow moving tropical systems we expect to see more often as a response to climate change. Upper level steering winds are slowing down over the continents during summer."[28]

Returning to the Harvey flooding situation, how did so much Gulf water end up in the streets of Houston? How does water vapor enter the picture? Answers probably lie in global warming dynamics.

Hurricane Harvey crossed the Gulf of Mexico in a matter of hours before making landfall. Somehow, Harvey scooped up a vast reservoir of water before it reached the Houston area. This extreme flooding likely required some extreme dynamics.

Much of what is happening in climate change today is foreign to 19th century climate behavior. Some specialists call it a new ballgame. For instance, historical patterns of ocean and atmospheric circulation have been significantly affected by rising global temperatures. Climate scientists are trying to catch up in an environment that is still changing in baffling ways. Exactly what happened when Harvey flooded Houston? One possibility is that a vicious cycle was involved to accelerate the extremely rapid evaporation of Gulf water. As noted earlier, a vicious cycle is an unstable dynamic that sometimes occurs in the chaos of nature. Several examples are included in this chapter.

According to a mid-2018 report, the amount of water that flooded Houston and surrounding areas of Harris County "exceeded every known flooding event in American history since 1899."[26] Hurricane Harvey dropped over 30 inches in two days, and nearly 50 inches over four days in some places. For the storm to produce that much rainfall would require an extremely moist atmosphere, which was perhaps replenished during the historic flooding. What physical process could manage to lift that quantity of Gulf water into the atmosphere in such a brief time?

Some answers to this question might include:

(a) An extremely high evaporation rate of Gulf water that loaded up the atmosphere with water vapor;

(b) A very high capacity of the atmosphere to hold water vapor and condensed water droplets (in clouds); and

(c) Some means to accelerate the water evaporation process beyond "business as usual." A vicious cycle was mentioned earlier as a possibility to accelerate the evaporation process.

With these elements in mind, a hypothetical explanation of the extreme flooding by Hurricane Harvey was constructed by this author. One part of the explanation is an illustration of plausible dynamics enabled by global warming. Another part is an outline of how other extreme flooding events might be at least partially explained.

The hypothetical explanation is illustrated in Figure 4-4 (on the next page). It is called the Transient Water Vapor Vicious Cycle. The cycle is transient because it is primarily active only while an intense hurricane or other massive storm is gaining strength during passage over a large, hot body of water. Figure 4-4 contains three subfigures, of which Figure 4c (vicious cycle) is the most important (Figures 4-4a and 4-4b support Figure 4-4c) This illustration provides one scenario in which Hurricane Harvey could have quickly gained enough moisture to put the Houston area under water in just a few days.

First, the vicious cycle loads up the atmosphere with maximum moisture and likely keeps it full as some moisture leaves the clouds as rainfall. Figures 4-4a and 4-4b explain how evaporation rate and vapor capacity can be amplified in supporting roles. Then, in Figure 4-4c, there is a sequence of dynamics that connect air temperature, vapor capacity, and evaporation rate. The result is a "moisture engine" producing extreme rainfall and flooding.

Does the above explanation for the Harvey hurricane flooding provide clues for future extreme flooding events? The main players in this hypothetical scenario are the vicious cycle, high atmospheric and ocean temperatures, and extreme evaporation rates and vapor capacities. The latter two factors are both dependent on temperature. As global warming continues to boost water and air temperatures, evaporation rates and H_2O

vapor capacity will automatically be boosted as well. The virtually certain expectation for the future is wetter storms and even more extreme flooding. Nature is constrained to behave according to its rules. Only human society has leverage to change the future of extreme flooding. For example, a rollback of atmospheric pollution could begin to reverse the global warming trend and thereby reduce the extreme flooding threat.

Figure 4-4.Transient Water Vapor Vicious Cycle*
*Feedbacks in a growing storm over ocean

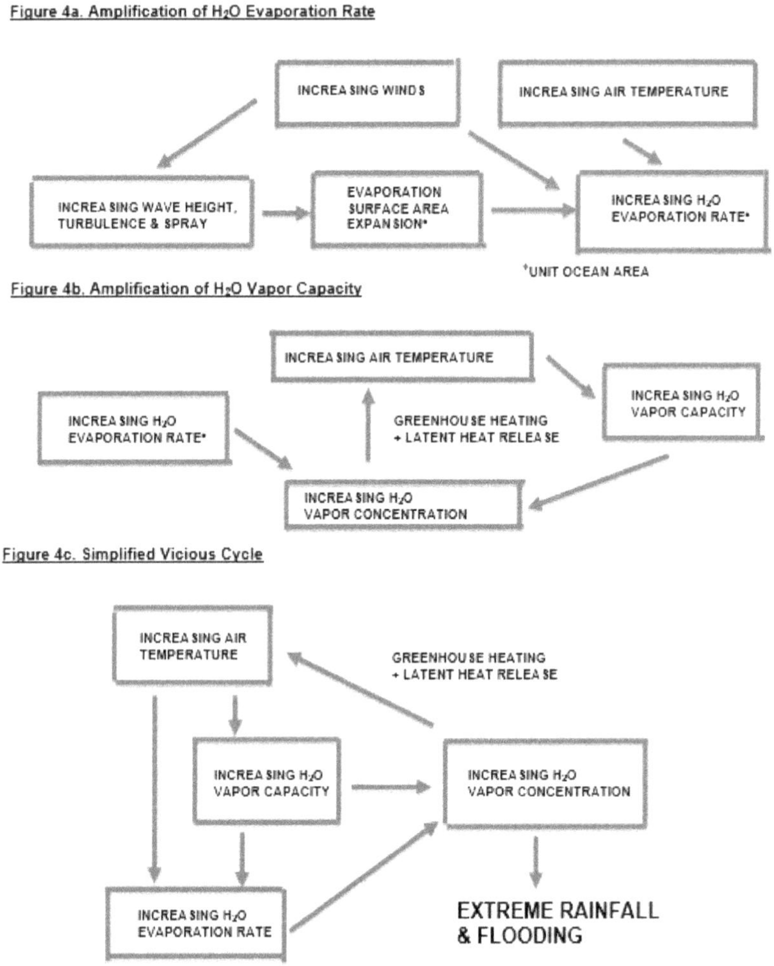

Figure 4a. Amplification of H_2O Evaporation Rate

INCREASING WINDS
INCREASING AIR TEMPERATURE
INCREASING WAVE HEIGHT, TURBULENCE & SPRAY
EVAPORATION SURFACE AREA EXPANSION*
INCREASING H_2O EVAPORATION RATE*
*UNIT OCEAN AREA

Figure 4b. Amplification of H_2O Vapor Capacity

INCREASING AIR TEMPERATURE
INCREASING H_2O VAPOR CAPACITY
INCREASING H_2O EVAPORATION RATE*
GREENHOUSE HEATING + LATENT HEAT RELEASE
INCREASING H_2O VAPOR CONCENTRATION

Figure 4c. Simplified Vicious Cycle

INCREASING AIR TEMPERATURE
GREENHOUSE HEATING + LATENT HEAT RELEASE
INCREASING H_2O VAPOR CAPACITY
INCREASING H_2O VAPOR CONCENTRATION
INCREASING H_2O EVAPORATION RATE
EXTREME RAINFALL & FLOODING

Vicious Cycle Traps Vulnerable Poor Nations (VPC)

A mid-2019 article in The Economist explained how vicious cycles can be found in the economics of adapting to climate change.[27.] Fundamental relations between climate change and survival economics for poor countries are shown in Figure 4-5. Poor countries are among the most vulnerable to climate change, and the least capable of affording protective adaptation measures.[27.]

A study by the U.N. Environmental Program estimated poor countries will need to spend $140–$300 billion per year on climate adaptive measures by 2030. Ironically, borrowing costs for poor counties are about 10% higher than for wealthy nations—partly due to climate risks.[27.] This interest rate premium puts needed adaptation measures even further out of reach. Climate adaptation costs could include building coastal defenses against rising seas; relocating coastal communities to higher ground; and recovery costs from extreme weather events (floods, droughts, wildfires, etc.).

As noted in Chapter 9, international aid to assist poor nations with climate adaptation costs is falling behind the $100 billion per year pledged as support. The U.N. study cited above forecasts adaptation costs will far exceed this pledged support level.

This concludes the nine stories that exemplify unstable climate dynamics.

Figure 4- 5. Climate Vicious Cycle For VPC*
*Vulnerable Poor Countries

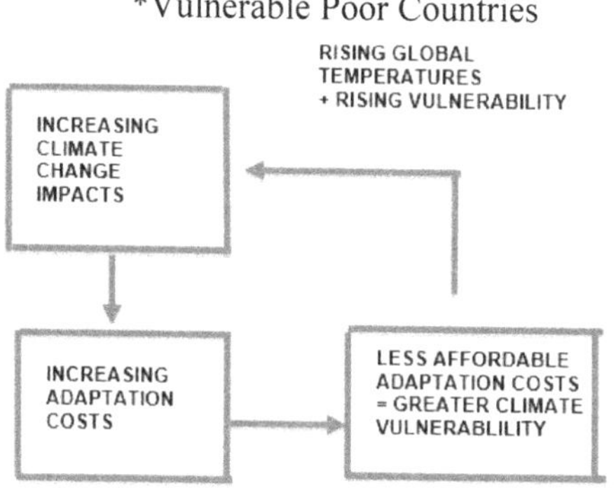

Chapter 4 Sources

1. Kaab, Andreas, 14 others, "Massive Collapse of Two Glaciers in Western Tibet in 2016 After Surge-Like Instability," Nature Geoscience, February, 2018, pp. 114–120 (I2192)

2. Pierre-Louis, Kendra, "Bigger Avalanches Being Triggered By Climate Change," New York Times, January 26, 2018, p. A8. (I2187)

3. Staff, "Arctic's Melting Ice Creates Vicious Circle," NSIDC in the News, June 9, 2016, p.1 (I2602)

4. Staff, "Overheated Arctic Sign of Climate Change 'Vicious Circle'", PHYS.ORG, November 24, 2016, pp. 1–3 (I2603)

5. L.S. Gardiner, "Sea Ice and Heat: A Vicious Cycle," L.S. Gardiner's Blog, September 10, 2012, p.1 (I2604)

6. Chelsea Harvey, "Antarctic Glaciers are Helping Drive Their Own Melt," Scientific American (E&E News), April 20, 2018, pp. 1–8. (I2563).

7. Alessandro Silvano et al., "Freshening by Glacial Meltwater Enhances Melting of Ice Shelves and Reduces Formation of Antarctic Bottom Water," AAAS Science Advances, April 18, 2018, Vol 4 no 4. (I2562)

8. (spare)

9. Ted Schuur, "The Permafrost Prediction," Scientific American, December, 2016. pp. 57–61 (I1913)

10. Henry Fountain, "Bigger Threat to Permafrost is Projected," New York Times, April 13, 2017, p. A7 (I2026)

11. Pierre-Louis, Kendra, "Beavers Thaw Permafrost As They Head Farther North," New York Times, December 21, 2017, p. A13 (I2176)

12. Jeff Masters, "The Jet Stream is Getting Weird," Scientific American, December, 2014, pp. 69–75 (I1501).

13. Quirin Schiermeier, "Atlantic Current Strength Declines," Nature/Scientific American, May 13, 2014 (I1969)

14. NOAA Web Site, "The Global Conveyor Belt," NOAA, July 10, 2013, p.1 (I1968)

15. Staff, "Familiar Weather Patterns are Thing of Past," Bulletin of the Atomic Scientists, Sept 19, 2016 (I1831)

16. Tim Wallace, "Nearly All the Globe's Excess Heat Is Going to One Place: The Oceans," New York Times, September 15, 2016, p. A6 (I1828).

17. Staff, "Davy Jones Heat Locker," The Economist, August 23, 2014, pp. 73-4 (I1459)

18. Staff, "Days of the Triffids," The Economist, November 12, 2016, p. 72 (I1910)

19. Jennifer Francis, "Rough Weather Ahead," Scientific American, June 2019, pp. 46–53 (I2549).

20. John Schwartz, "Heavy Rain, Catastrophic Floods, and Complications of Climate Change," New York Times, March 23, 2019, p. A12 (I2514)

21. John Schwartz, "In NOAA's Forecast, Flooding 'worse than anything we've seen in recent years,'" New York Times, March 22, 2019, p. A18 (I2513)

22. David Leonhardt, "The Story of 2018 was Climate Change," New York Times, December 31, 2018, p. A23 (I2475)

23. John Schwartz, "More Floods, More Droughts: Climate Change Delivers Both," New York Times, December 13, 2018, p. A8 (I2468)

24. John Schwartz, "Like a Terror Movie: How Changing Climate Will Multiply Disasters," New York Times, November 20, 2018 (I2442)

25. Staff, "Stormy Weather," The Economist, September 22, 2018, pp. 54–5. (I2290)

26. Kendra Pierre-Louis, "Storms Linger, Growing More Dangerous" New York Times, June 8, 2018, p. A15 (I2227)

27. Staff, "Costing the Earth," The Economist, August 17, 2019, p. 57 (I2605)

28. John Schwartz, "Mass of Clouds Provides Clearer View of Effects From Changing Climate," New York Times, September 4, 2019, p. A12 (I2606).

29. Veronica Penney, "5 Ways Climate is Changing Hurricanes," New York Times, November 11, 2020, p. A19 (I2926)

30. Henry Fountain, "Warming May Be Giving Hurricanes Life Over Land", New York Times, November 12, 2020, p. A25 (I2927)

Chapter 5:
Global Warming Impacts on the Biosphere

A few impacts of global warming have already been noted incidentally in previous chapters. This chapter expands on such examples to convey what is known about how global warming and climate change are making differences to the planet. This chapter also includes a discussion of weather attribution science, which analyzes causes of extreme weather events. Chapters 6 and 7 focus on principal climate threats to life on Earth.

Global Warming Impacts

Compared to the traditional weather and climate before the mid-19th century, what is new and different about current weather and climate? There are actually a number of differences, enabled only by the unprecedented escalation of global temperatures. The following are eleven ways the situation has worsened because of global warming.

(1) One new way is known simply as "The Blob." This new feature of the ocean environment is caused by an extreme marine heat wave that quickly stabilizes in an area, resulting in far-above-normal ocean temperatures. "Blobs" can persist for days or years, and besides impacting regional weather adversely, they are deadly to salmon, sea lions and other wildlife.[1] This new phenomenon has been the subject of formal attribution studies, as reported in the journal Science (climate attribution science is discussed later in this chapter). According to marine scientist Charlotte Laufkoter of the University of Bern, Switzerland, these "blob" events will likely increase along with rising global temperatures.[1]

(2) Another new climate feature, also in the world's oceans, is the recent discovery of large carbon deposits poised to release CO_2 and methane into the atmosphere. Many of these marine carbon deposits are held by frozen hydrate caps, and some are in seawater that is close to the thawing point.[2.] These large carbon deposits represent grave risks for amplified climate

disasters.[2] Among the uncertainties associated with this threat are the number and size of yet-to-be-detected marine carbon reserves. This threat is examined further in Chapter 7.

(3) Two recent medical studies have concluded children are more at risk than adults to suffer from air pollution-related diseases.[3] Future warming and air pollution will be especially harmful to children because they spend more time outdoors and their young lungs are more vulnerable to fine particles associated with wildfires and other pollution sources. One study was reported in the New England Journal of Medicine and the other reported in The Lancet.[3] Dr. Renee Salas of the Harvard Medical School observed that "[w]ith every degree of warming, a child born today faces a future where their health and well-being will be increasingly impacted by the realities and dangers of a warming world."[3]

(4) Climate disasters are less often singular events and more often occur as cascading or multiple events.[4,5,6] A new term used by scientists is "compound extremes," in which a sequence of disasters makes matters worse for the next disaster.[4] An example is a severe drought that parches the landscape, followed by an expansive wildfire that scorches the landscape, followed by extreme rainfall that floods the now-muddy landscape. During the 2020 Climate Week in New York City, Florida was drowning under a slow-moving hurricane while the American West was battling fire tornadoes.[6] Experts call such multiple disasters "a preview of life under climate change."[5]

(5) Rising sea levels are already impacting home mortgages and insurance policies in affected communities. Exceptionally large and intense wildfires are having a similar effect.[7] Thirty-year mortgages in such communities are being replaced by shorter term and interest only loans. Flood and fire insurance are becoming mandatory in high-risk locales. Another growing trend is banks selling loans to federal entities under the terms of which taxpayers are liable to cover losses. Homes and other properties in vulnerable areas are losing market value. Losses could escalate to catastrophic when climate change encounters tipping points. No such threats existed before global warming.

(6) "Warmer Climate Raises Risk of Dam Disasters" reads a newspaper headline.[8] This, too, is a new concern related to climates being altered by rising temperatures. A common reason for dam failure is too much water being impounded behind the dam. This is how a dam in central Michigan failed in May 2020[8.] The dam, (in Edenville Township -- 30 miles upstream from Midland, MI), was one of 170 in Michigan classified as having high hazard potential. There are about 15,500 dams in the U.S. in that category. "We should expect more of these down the road" according to civil engineering professor Amir Aghakouchak of the University of California, Irving.[8.]

The dam failure in central Michigan followed a series of saturating rains that pushed a swollen Tittabawassee River against a dam designed a century earlier—before global warming enabled extreme rainfalls.[8.] It would not be surprising if the rate of dam failures were to increase as global warming continues unabated. Persons living below those 15,500 risky dams in the U.S. should take note. Others living below risky dams around the world should also take note.

(7) A new term for the 21st-century climate is "flash drought."[9] NOAA has described this as "a potent combination of record-breaking heat and lack of rain." One of these flash droughts gripped the Tennessee and Ohio River valleys in September/October 2019. This disaster was preceded by extreme rainfall. In other words, these river communities were sandwiched between two extremes![9.]

The NOAA National Weather Services' Climate Prediction Center defines flash drought as "an event during which an area experiences degradation by two or more drought categories in a four week period." The severe flash drought in the Tennessee and Ohio River valleys escalated rapidly, and is representative of how climate disasters have magnified under the lens of global warming. Flash droughts are also discussed in Chapter 6.

(8) Recent research has discovered a new downside to extreme weather and climate disasters: deadly toxins buried slightly underground are being uncovered and spread around.[10] For example, Hurricane Maria stirred up

PCBs in Puerto Rico, causing a tripling of airborne PCBs. People exposed to contaminants once buried in soil risk being infected with ailments including cancer and respiratory diseases[10]. Professor of Environmental Health Naresh Kumar, of the University of Miami, warns: "We are sitting on a pile of toxic poisons…whenever we have these natural disasters, they are stirred."[10] Other research into Hurricane Harvey and California wildfires found dislodged contaminants included sewage, asbestos, and heavy metals.[10].

(9) Another distinct change from the late 19th-early 20th century is that heat waves have turned more deadly, longer-lasting and more frequent.[11] The death toll from the Chicago heat wave in 1995 exceeded 700 souls. Heat waves in the U.S. now last 45 days longer, on average, than in the 1960s. The annual number of heat waves in the U.S. has tripled since the '60s.[11]. Scientific attribution studies have determined climate change is behind worsening heat waves.[12]

(10) Climate change, itself, is new to the post–18th–century environment. Before climate change, there was just climate. Weather statistics provided a stable basis for characterizing a region's climate. Not much changed between decades or between centuries. Enter unprecedented global warming and constant climate change. Once predictable, climate has become difficult to predict.[13] For example, "weather makers" like the jet stream and named ocean currents are now less predictable. Climate changes beget changes. Global warming enables new situations like vicious cycles which can quickly change a region's climate. New climate conditions in the Arctic are an example. Change can produce instabilities, and instabilities can render new uncertainty. Nature is capable of non-linearity and even chaos. Therein lies loss of predictability.

(11) Big changes are happening in the largest portions of Earth's surface: the oceans. For example, the oceans have absorbed 93% of the excess heat caused by global warming. This heat build-up over the past 170 years is causing significant changes to the oceans, their living occupants, and bordering shores.[14,15] The oceans absorb about 25% of polluting carbon dioxide, which increases ocean acidity far above normal. The impact to sea

creatures like coral is disastrous. Many of the beautiful coral reefs that existed before the 20th century are sick, turning ghostly gray and dying. That is a great loss to many fish species dependent on coral for food. Concerns for the current and future state of Earth's oceans are explained in a special report of the Intergovernmental Panel on Climate Change (IPCC). Scientists and policy makers from 36 countries produced the report.[15.]

These eleven instances of new conditions in the Earth's biosphere exemplify global warming's impacts.

Weather Attribution Science

Causes of severe weather events (such as record temperatures, extreme rainfall, catastrophic storms, and devastating droughts) can be natural and/or global warming/climate change. The science of analyzing those causes is called weather attribution.

There is a hierarchy of generic possibilities:

Global warming and climate change are:

The sole cause of a severe weather event

The principal cause " " "

A major cause " " "

A secondary cause " " "

Not a cause " " "

Another possibility is that global warming and climate change cannot be reasonably blamed for causing specific weather events, but can be blamed for the frequency and/or intensity of such events.

A third possibility is that attribution science is unable to discern causes of specific weather events or types of events. This last possibility was the situation before the dawn of attribution science. It can still be the situation in some cases, but now more rarely, as the science has matured.

Before describing the science of weather attribution, the general scientific approach is reviewed for the benefit of readers who lack a science background. Scientific work is highly precise and rigorous compared to many occupations. Guesswork and imprecision are unscientific. Precise measurements of phenomena in a natural or laboratory environment are preferred. Theoretical estimates are acceptable when empirical data are not available, as are quantitative probability or likelihood values. Empirical data are measurements of the environment or events in the environment (for example, inside a tornado).

There is a de facto code of scientific conduct that includes mutual cooperation to establish the best available evidence and analysis. This means scientists share and coordinate their work with other scientists.

Residual uncertainties, analysis limitations, and sensor measurement parameters are identified as qualifications to conclusions reached. No cheating. No fake evidence. No exaggeration. Further, a scientist's work is not considered acceptable until accepted by other specialists in the field (a process called peer review). Scientists are expected to "follow the science." That means accepting what nature reveals rather than unchallenged or biased notions. In other words, scientists are expected to remain completely objective. Scientific rigor is maintained by globally-connected scientists. Research reported in scientific journals is commonly authored by several collaborating scientists (sometimes numbering 40 or more). Journal editors also assure the reported works have followed good scientific practice.

What does all this mean for the science of weather attribution? It means fair, honest, and careful investigation of causes behind severe weather. It means climate investigations "follow the science" rather than to prove arbitrary claims. Reputable scientists stake their reputations on their work and on acceptance by peers. This concludes comments on the scientific approach. Weather attribution science is described next.

Dr. Friederike Otto of The Royal Meteorological Society has described[16] a common approach to attribution of an extreme weather event, which is to use "state-of-the-art climate models and statistical methods" to compare:

(1) the likelihood of that event in today's climate with

(2) the likelihood of that event in the climate that existed before climate change (before the Industrial Revolution).

Fortunately, good weather statistics are available for computing the two numerical likelihoods. Dr. Otto offers this example: the European highest temperature record of 40°C today could now be expected once every 10 years. Before the Industrial Revolution it was expected once every 100 years. In other words, climate change has made the European record temperature event "10 times more likely."[16.]

The rigorous process of computing weather event likelihoods takes considerable care and time, so calculation results might not be available until months after the events. For example, official attribution analysis of 2018 extreme weather events was not reported until December 2019.[17] This U.S. government report compiled 21 peer-reviewed research efforts from 121 scientists in 13 countries.

Some conclusions of the report: Human-caused climate change increased the likelihood of 2018 extreme events, notably flooding in Mid-Atlantic states, heat waves in northeast Asia and the Iberian peninsula, intense drought in the Four Corners area; and record-low sea ice in the Bering Sea. National Oceanic and Atmospheric Agency (NOAA) scientist Stephanie Heering, editor of the report, remarked: "This year we are also seeing mounting evidence for our ability to identify a climate change signal in different types of extreme weather events, especially for forest fires and precipitation."[17]

Among the 2018 extreme weather findings are:

** Climate change makes nighttime heat waves like that experienced in northeast China at least 8 times more frequent.

** Climate change makes extreme flooding like that in the Mid-Atlantic states 50% more likely.

** The extreme fire season in Queensland Australia and the intense drought in the U.S. Southwest were more severe or more likely due to climate change.

This NOAA climate report followed one from the World Meteorological Organization (WMO), released three months earlier.[18.] The WMO report warned of increased greenhouse gas concentrations and their impacts, which were attributed to climate change. WMO Secretary-General Petteri Taalas is concerned "climate change causes and impacts are increasing." The WMO report "highlights the urgency and the potential of ambitious climate action in order to limit potentially irreversible impacts."[18.] This "irreversible impacts" concern was echoed recently in the journal Nature by scientists warning of "abrupt and irreversible changes, or tipping points.[19] These tipping point concerns underscore the necessity and urgency of the work of weather attribution scientists.

The few examples of weather attribution studies cited here are among many such examples. One recent example is the finding that global warming made the Australian wildfires at least 30% more likely.[20] Recent and future attribution examples can be accessed at worldweatherattribution.org.[21]

While more examples of dismal climate concerns could have been included in this chapter, a fair balance should at least acknowledge some significant progress in combating climate change. A sampling of such progress is listed below:[22.]

(a) The Yale Program on Climate Change Communication reports over 50% of Americans are now convinced of climate urgency, while "doubtful" and "dismissive" groups have declined to 18% of the population.

(b) The costs of carbon-free, renewable energy are now competitive with those of coal and other polluting fossil fuel.

(c) New species are being discovered and others are being rediscovered to help offset those species facing extinction.

(d) Conservationists are winning court battles to protect the Arctic, federal lands in five Western states, and various wildlife.

(e) Oil corporations are developing and implementing ways to capture and store carbon rather than release it into the environment.

The positive proposals in Chapter 11 to slow global warming and eliminate carbon emissions can be added to the above list if those (or similar) proposals are accepted and implemented by society.

Chapter 5 Sources

1. Henry Fountain, "Scientists Tie Deadly Heat 'Blob' in the Pacific to Climate Change," New York Times, September 25, 2020, p. A13 (I2906)

2. Todd Woody, "Hugh Amount of Greenhouse Gases Lurk in the Oceans and Could Make Warming Far Worse," National Geographic.com, December 17, 2019, pp. 1-3 (I2722)

3. Kendra Pierre-Louis, "Climate Change to Have Harsh Effect on Children," New York Times, November 14, 2019, p.A9 (I2783)

4. Damien Cave, "Drought, Fire, Deluge: Climate's Multiplier Effect Pounds Australia," New York Times, February 24, 2020, p. A4 (I2802)

5. Christopher Flavelle, Henry Fountain, "Pileup of Disasters Reflects Reality of Climate Change," New York Times, August 5, 2020, p. A21 (I2864)

6. Somini Sengupta, "At Climate Week, America's Cascading Disasters Take Center Stage," New York Times, September 26, 2020, p. A13 (I2908)

7. Christopher Flavelle, "Climate Change is Transforming the Time-Honored Home Loan," New York Times, June 20, 2020, p. A21 (I2845)

8. Henry Fountain, "'Expect More of These': Warmer Climate Raises Risk of Dam Disasters," New York Times, May 22, 2020 (I2826)

9. Tom DiLiberto, "Flash Drought Engulfs the U.S. Southeast in September 2019," NOAA Climate.gov, October 9, 2019, pp. 1–5 (I2673)

10. Christopher Flavelle, "In Disaster's Wake, a Stew of Toxins Bubble Up," New York Times, July 16, 2019, p. A10 (I2586)

11. Kendra Pierre-Louis, "Climate Change Bolsters the Threat of Heat Waves," New York Times, July 19, 2019, p. A18. (I2589)

12. Henry Fountain, "Air Mass That Wilted Europe Moves to Greenland," New York Times, August 3, 2019, p. A7. (I2601)

13. Staff, "Throwing the Dice," The Economist, September 21, 2019, pp. 83–85 (I2655)

14. Staff, "Sea Changes," The Economist, September 28, 2019, p. 57 (I2665)

15. Brad Plumer, "Warming Poses Grave Danger to World's Oceans", New York Times, September 26, 2019, pp. 1,9. (I2663)

16. Friederike Otto, "Attribution of Extreme Weather Events: How Does Climate Change Affect Weather?" Royal Meteorological Society, September 9, 2018, pp 1–3 (I2759)

17. American Meteorological Society, "New Research Examines Climate Change's Role in 2018 Extreme Weather Events" NASA, December 9, 2019, pp. 1–6 (I2786)

18. Staff, "The Global Climate in 2015-2019: Climate Changes Accelerate," World Meteorological Organization (WMO), September 22, 2019, pp. 1-5 (I2714)

19. Henry Fountain, "A World Speeding 'Dangerously Close' to a Tipping Point," New York Times, December 5, 2019, p. A10 (I2711)

20. Henry Fountain, "Warming Contributed to Wildfires, Study Finds," New York Times, March 5, 2020, p. A6 (I2806)

21. Staff, "World Weather Attribution," World Weather Attribution.org, March 18, 2020 (I2808)

22. Margaret Renkl, "(Some) Hope for the Environment," New York Times, March 17, 2021, p. A23 (I3030)

Introduction to Chapters Six and Seven

Chapters Six and Seven summarize the climate threats that are likely the most dangerous. These are growing threats made worse as global temperatures continue to increase. Exactly how these threats will evolve depends on currently unknown factors such as future climate action plans and when climate tipping points might be encountered. Also, many climate dynamics are exponential (as explained in Chapter 2) and such non-linearity can force explosive change. Certain facts are known: climate change is deadly and it is killing even the ecosystems upon which the survival of all forms of life depends. A few examples are noted below.

**Species extinction is not uncommon in itself, but the current accelerating rate is both uncommon and alarming. The number of extinctions that used to occur in a full century are now happening yearly.[1] Habitat loss and wildlife trade are traditional culprits, but according to Dr. Gerado Ceballos, lead author of a recent study reported by the National Academy of Sciences, climate change "has yet to unleash 'the full tsunami' of its impacts.'" Rebecca Shaw, Chief Scientist at World Wildlife Fund, commented:[1.]

"Ceballos and his colleagues are telling us with scientific certainty that the survival of these species is linked to our own survival."

**Bumblebees, vital to agricultural pollination, are wholesale victims of climate change.[2] A recent study found their population in North America had plummeted 46% compared to the base period of 1901–1974. A lead author of the study, Peter Soroye of the University of Ottawa, observed: "This group of organisms is such a critical pollinator in wild landscapes and agricultural regions."[2]

**Due to climate change, 200 reindeer starved to death when the vegetation they fed on was covered by ice. Climate change altered rainfall intensity and frequency in the High Arctic, and soaked snow turned to ice.[3]

Terrestrial ecologist Ashild Onvik Pedersen of the Norwegian Polar Institute explained: "Once you get the rain on top of the snow, most often it completely freezes to solid ice that completely covers the plants."[3]

The climate threats described in these two chapters are consequences of global warming and climate change. Global warming started about the same time reliable instruments to accurately measure atmospheric weather parameters became available—about 140 years ago. Specific impacts of global warming/climate change on weather, climate, human safety, etc. are examined in these chapters. Both impacts of record and predicted impacts from future warming are included.

Global warming is both changing climates in fundamental ways and impacting everyday weather. The U.S. government tracks global weather statistics, and relevant agencies prepare a National Climate Assessment report summarizing warming impacts.[4] That research and documentation activity was described in the latest report: "Thousands of studies conducted by tens of thousands of scientists around the world have documented changes in surface, atmosphere, and oceanic temperatures; melting glaciers; disappearing snow cover; shrinking sea ice; rising sea level; and an increase in atmospheric water vapor. Rainfall patterns and storms are changing and the occurrence of droughts is shifting."[4] This 669-page National Climate Assessment (NCA) is a reliable information source on climate change, and it is referenced liberally in these two chapters.

Some folks seem to think that climate change is not relevant to current environmental dangers - that climate change threats really matter only in the distant future. (See source # 52 in Chapter 6 Sources). These folks are mistaken. Climate change is making severe weather more extreme. More deadly. More frequent. More damaging. Climate change is also making wildfires more devastating - ending lives and livelihoods.

Are these folks unaware of climate change's assault on our ecosystems? Killing whole species needed for biodiversity and balance for all species to thrive. One example is coral reefs. Climate change is causing higher ocean temperatures and acidity, making it often impossible for some coral reefs to survive. Are these folks unaware that coral reefs are critical for maintaining the seafood chain? The reefs also supply much of the oxygen that humans and other animals breathe.

Chapters 6 and 7 set the record straight. Climate change is definitely relevant to current environmental dangers. It is even dangerous to the global economy. These two chapters should be a wake-up call on the need for immediate and aggressive action to combat climate change. Avoidance and mitigation of a carbon emissions surge (Chapter 2) is another excellent reason for such action.

The brief discussions in chapters 6 and 7 provide glimpses of climate threats that continue to worsen. These stories do not end here. Readers are encouraged to explore the listed sources for additional information and to remain vigilant as new information becomes available in the public domain.

Chapter 6 begins on the next page.

Chapter 6: Climate Threats. Part One

The climate threats discussed in this chapter are:

Extreme air temperature

Extreme precipitation and flooding

Extreme drought

Wildfires

Severe storms

Rising sea levels

Receding mountain glaciers

Extreme Air Temperature

Extreme heat fatalities in the over-65 age group have grown 50% in the last 20 years. This is according to a report published by The Lancet.[5] Total worldwide deaths from extreme heat in that age group equaled 296,000 in 2018 (mostly in Asia and parts of Europe). Experts from 35 research groups contributed to The Lancet report, which covered food security, infectious disease, air pollution and other heat-related factors affecting public health. The authors also stressed the need for "vast reductions" in carbon emissions in the next few years, saying, "These next five years will be pivotal."[5.]

Heat tops the list of weather-related deaths in the United States— ahead of flooding, tornadoes, hurricanes and lightning (in that order).[6] The 30-year average for annual heat fatalities is 134, followed by floods at 85 fatalities. In 2017, the number of heat exposure deaths in Arizona and Nevada soared to 235 and 139, respectively.[7] Projected U.S. heat fatalities are expected to number in the "tens of thousands" by the year 2100. Extreme heat is expected to render parts of the Middle East and North Africa "uninhabitable" by the same year.[7]

Air temperature is one of the most important weather parameters, and it is directly affected by global warming. When measured air temperature at Earth's surface is averaged over the whole globe and over an entire year, it is easy to track temperature changes from year to year. That computation was briefly described in Chapter 2. As mentioned, accurate temperature measurements have been available for about 140 years, so it is possible to tabulate annual surface temperatures over that time span. Incidentally, the industrial age and air pollution have been most active during approximately the same time period.

Global warming makes the coldest climates measurably warmer, and the hottest climates unbearable to dangerously hot. Temperatures in the United States are projected to continue rising, as is the incidence of worldwide extreme heat events.[4] Record-breaking temperatures are also occurring more frequently.[4] Arctic temperatures are rising at about double the average global rate, and the Arctic Ocean is expected to be nearly ice-free in late summer before 2040.[4]

The year 2018 was the fourth hottest year since 1880, and 18 of the 19 highest average annual surface temperatures have all been recorded since 2001.[8] During a recent extreme heat wave in Montréal, Canada (and nearby communities), 70 people died of heatstroke—so many the city morgue's capacity was exceeded.[9]

Heat waves are lasting longer and reaching higher temperatures.[10] Research conducted by the Union of Concerned Scientists (UCS) concluded dangerous heat waves will intensify sharply in the next decades (in the absence of effective reduction of greenhouse emissions). A senior UCS climate scientist warns that "within the next 30 years, many people in the United States will be faced with heat unlike any they've felt before."[10] Heat waves in nearly 300 urban centers will cause "at least 30 days extreme heat per year with a heat index above 105 degrees Fahrenheit."[10]

Extreme Precipitation and Flooding

Rain and snow are the precipitation types considered here. Too much rain in a brief time interval causes flooding and/or mudslides. Too little rain drains freshwater reservoirs and deprives crops of needed irrigation. Too little snow affects mountain glacier survival (Chapter 1); snowpack water resources and snow recreation availability/economics.

According to a new data analysis, flooding risks, which follow extreme rainfall, are much greater than previously thought.[11] Extreme rainfall events are very likely to continue increasing over most the globe.[4] In Australia, the devastating floods from extreme rainfall are now considered the new normal.[12] One such event in Spring 2021 resulted from two merging storms that dropped 36 inches of rain in five days. This closed over 150 schools, and 20,000 people had to be evacuated. Andy Pitman at the University of New South Wales advises: "There's good scientific evidence to say extreme rain is becoming more extreme due to global warming."[12]

Monsoon flooding in Nepal killed 67 people in July 2019.[51] On the southern margins of snowy areas, the current trend is decreased snowstorm frequency and an earlier snowmelt season.[4] Future projections of snow packs in the Western United States indicate large declines, whereas in the central and eastern parts, more snow will fall as rain.[4] Extreme one-day rainfall has increased 80% in the United States since 1990.[13] Annual flooding costing over $1 billion in damage hit the following areas:[13]

- Michigan and parts of northeast
- South Carolina, Texas and Oklahoma
- Louisiana, West Virginia and Houston

Extreme flooding in Spring 2019 inundated the northern plains in the United States.[14] According to the Des Moines Register, 17 levees failed to contain the Missouri River in Iowa, Nebraska, and Missouri. Some towns were completely submerged, and even the National Weather Service office in Valley, Nebraska had to be evacuated.[14] Governor Pete Ricketts estimated losses in Nebraska alone would exceed $1.3 billion, including $440 million in crop losses.[14] A long-term problem for farmers was nutrient-rich topsoil being washed away into the Missouri and Mississippi Rivers.[14]

Deke Arndt, a NOAA climate scientist, noted major flooding "is an expected and observed consequence of climate change."[15] Extreme rainfall events are very likely to continue increasing.[4] The U.S. Environmental Protection Agency (EPA) recently reported that climate change is gaining speed, making matter worse. One such instance is that climbing temperatures are responsible for newly spreading Lyme disease.[16]

Climate change doubled the probability of extreme flooding in a 2-day storm that hit eastern South Africa on April11, 2022.[53] Rainfall totaled 14 inches in some places, killing over 400 people and devastating homes and transportation infrastructure. President Cyril Ramaphosa called the flooding "the biggest tragedy we have ever seen". Izidine Pinto, co-author of the study that pinned the blame on climate change, remarked: "We need to drastically reduce greenhouse gas emissions and adapt to a new reality where floods and heat waves are more intense and damaging".[53]

Extreme Drought

The persistent absence of precipitation, otherwise known as drought, is another condition of weather and climate. Drought severity can depend on how long the condition persists and how hot average temperatures are—both of which factors can be affected by global warming and climate change. Shifting climate patterns can literally rewrite precipitation statistics for an area or region. Climbing temperatures are likely to worsen drought severity when it occurs. According to the National Climate Assessment, precipitation extremes (rainfall or drought) "have already become more frequent, intense, or of longer duration, and many extremes are expected to continue to increase or worsen."[4]

As this was being written, the southeast United States was hit by a "flash drought."[17] Usually droughts are caused by dry conditions over an extended period, but a flash drought follows a briefer period of exceptional dryness and exceptionally high temperatures. NOAAClimate.gov advises that this combination quickly evaporates soil moisture.[17] Agricultural impacts of a flash drought can include reduced water supplies, degraded pasture conditions and less-than-ideal planting and harvesting conditions.[17] An agricultural periodical, Modern Farmer, reported temperatures 9–12 degrees above normal from Northern Florida to Virginia, including Kentucky, Georgia, and North Carolina (which all reported record highs).[18]

The flash drought in the Southeast U.S. evolved into a "megadrought" that might rival historic droughts of the ancient past.[19] Climate change is estimated to be responsible for about one-half of this drought's severity. Intense heat is compounding the drought situation, and the affected area is expanding because of an effect called "self-intensification."[20] Drought dynamics are affected not only by high temperatures and the absence of rainfall, but also by factors such as soil moisture, wind, humidity, and cloud cover.[21.]

According to a study published in the journal Nature Climate Change, this megadrought has become the driest in at least 1200 years and 2000-2021 was the driest within the modern record.[54] This historic drought was pushed to extremes, in part, by human-caused warming.[54] Dan Collins, a meteorologist at National Oceanic and Atmospheric Administration, said this drought could expand into areas such as south-central Arizona and southeast Texas.[55] The drought is also impacting mountain snowpacks. California's snowpack shrunk 23% since 2021 and now stands at just 39% of average.[56] These winter conditions are expected to worsen with future climate change.[56]

Aside from agricultural impacts, severe droughts can worsen deadly wildfires, stress hydroelectric power grids, and even affect river levels needed for barge transportation.[22] According to one study, disruption of food production can create unrest, leading to forced migrations.[22] A more recent study published in Nature confirmed concerns that future droughts' reduction of soil moisture will threaten food security.[23] This study also confirmed the connection between jobs and climate change.[23]

The U.S. government publishes a weekly drought monitor map that charts drought severity on five levels between "abnormally dry" and "exceptional drought."[24] One step below exceptional drought is extreme drought, whose possible impacts are "major crop/pasture losses; widespread water shortages or restrictions." Exceptional drought's impacts are more extreme, and include water emergencies from shortages in reservoirs, streams, and wells.[24] Risks of such drought impacts are expected to rise as the Earth's thermostat is pushed upward by growing pollution.

Wildfires

According to Jonathan Overpeck, Professor of Geosciences, Hydrology, and Atmospheric Sciences at the University of Arizona, "there are multiple reasons why wildfires are getting more severe and destructive, but climate change tops the list."[25] He notes that the latest U.S. National Climate Assessment (NCA) predicts that by 2050, the area devastated annually in Western United States "could be two to six times larger than today."[25] This NCA also cautions those wildfires could cause "profound changes to certain ecosystems."[4] The NCA further warns of future "compound events" when "multiple extreme climate events occur simultaneously or sequentially."[4] One such compound event could be the coupling of extreme droughts with extreme wildfires and extreme temperatures—a sort of "Hell on Earth."

The growing wildfire threat from a warming planet has been known for some time. The renowned American Association for the Advancement of Science (AAAS) published an overview of climate change threats in early 2014.[26] Of wildfire threats, this study noted: "Climate change has amplified the threat of wildfires in many places. In the western United States, both the area burned by wildfires and the length of the fire season have increased substantially in recent decades." The study also warned of increasing threat of "mega-fires" burning greater areas.[26]

An example of climate change affecting wildfire risk is 1989's Hurricane Hugo, which damaged 4.39 million acres of forest in South Carolina. That damage left behind considerable fuel for the next wildfire.[27] But the reverse is also true. Wildfires add to climate change risk, as "the burning of trees, dead biomass and soil sends high pulses of carbon to the atmosphere."[27] This interaction is similar to the vicious cycles noted in Chapter 4 in perpetuating global warming and climate change.

Eleven forest fires since the year 2000 have destroyed homes and infrastructure, contributing to over $1 billion losses each wildfire season.[28] Between 1986 and 2003, wildfires in the Western U.S. burned more than six times the area and lasted five times longer than during the period between 1970 and 1986.[29] Nevertheless, the climate change issue is often sidestepped by political candidates, and differences of opinion tend to fall on party lines.[30] A Pew Center poll measured a 38-point gap between Democrats and Republicans on whether the U.S. should do "whatever it takes" to protect the environment.[30]

The growing wildfire threat is a global phenomenon. Large fires are burning in places where they were previously rare. Arctic Siberia is one example.[31] Extraordinary fires are also burning in the Amazon basin, the central African savanna, and Indonesian rainforests. Many of these fires were intentionally set for agricultural purposes, but can be difficult to keep under control.

Arson and downed power lines are among human activities causing most wildfires, but lightning-triggered wildfires are gaining more notice. The U.S. Forest Service estimates western U.S. wildfires set by lightning between 1992 and 2015 are responsible for 71% of the area burned by all wildfires.[32] Besides causing more lightning, climate change is enabling greater lightning impact by removing moisture from the soil and vegetation.[32] Scientist David Romps of UC Berkeley notes that "we might expect to get 50% more lightning if greenhouse emissions are not slashed."[32]

Another threat of wildfires to humans is the adverse effects from breathing fine particulate matter in the smoke.[33] Among known effects are severe asthma, heart and lung disease, and irregular heartbeats. Inhaling fine particles from all pollution sources (including wildfires) was estimated to cause 4.2 million premature deaths worldwide in 2016.[33]

A new United Nations report released in February 2022[57] finds that climate change continues to raise major wildfire risks and it labeled this threat a "global wildfire crisis". Produced by 50 researchers from six continents, the report estimates these risks could amplify by up to 57% by 2100. Fire expert Clynis Humphrey says "There isn't the right attention to fire from governments".[57] The report asserts extraordinary wildfire risks will increase significantly even if carbon emissions are limited. Future wildfires could even convert rainforests from carbon sinks to carbon sources.[58] Another consequence of frequent megafires is that they are rendering important tools for managing water resources less accurate.[56]

An example of the growing wildfire risk are the many fires now burning in the Southwest of the U.S..[59] The biggest fire is the largest ever in New Mexico's recorded history. About one-half of some 6,000 firefighters in the region are fighting the over 300,000 acre New Mexico blaze.[59]

An example of a changing wildfire risk is the greater risk to U.S. homes.[60] New data released by the non-profit First Street Foundation has calculated risk for houses across the continental U.S. One aspect of this changing risk is that rising home prices in metropolitan areas is forcing migration into more fire-prone areas.[60] Also, climate change is contributing to greater wildfire frequency and intensity.[60]

The future for wildfires is not hopeful if global warming continues unchecked. Hotter, drier conditions will increase wildfire potential, according to Professor John Abatzoglou of the Department of Geography at the University of Idaho. He forecasts a continued warming trend, which means a growing risk of "large, uncontainable fires globally."[34] January 2022 was the sixth warmest January in the last 143 years according to NOAA data.[55]

Severe Storms

There are at least two fundamental reasons why global warming is responsible for increasing storm severity. (1) Heat is a form of energy, and higher ocean and air temperatures mean more energetic storms. The extra energy is demonstrated by higher wind speeds. For example, Category 2 and 3 hurricanes can intensify towards higher categories. (2) Warmer air holds more water vapor, which, in turn, enables extreme rainfall and flooding. The general rule is that for each 1°C rise in air temperature, the atmosphere can hold 7% more water vapor.[35] Global warming is likely one reason Hurricane Harvey flooded the streets of Houston Texas (see Chapter 4). The National Climate Assessment (NCA) states: "Temperature and precipitation extremes can affect...the likelihood of disasters. Some extremes have already become more frequent, intense, or of longer duration, and many extremes are expected to continue to increase or worsen."[4] The NCA also states: "Both physics and numerical modeling simulations (in general) indicate an increase in tropical cyclone intensity in a warmer world, and the models generally show increase in the number of very intense tropical cyclones."[4] The number of multiple Category 4 and 5 hurricanes in a single year has increased substantially in recent decades (see Chapter 4). The Journal of Climate published a study in 2018 which indicated "winds inside hurricanes are getting stronger."[36] More deadly storms in the future are a sobering prospect considering how deadly severe storms have been in the past. Bangladesh lost between 300,000 and 500,000 people when Cyclone Bhola struck in 1970. The Philippines lost 6,300 people in 2013 to Cyclone Haiyan.[37] Aside from fatalities, many millions are displaced from their homes by floods and storms. According to the Internal Displacement Monitoring Center, an average of over 20 million people have been displaced by storms each year during the past decade.[38]

Severe storms are not only intensifying, but they also seem to be evolving in new and dangerous ways. A recent example is Category 5 Hurricane Dorian, which battered the Bahamas after stalling in place for 24 hours.[39] Dr. Jennifer Francis, a senior scientist at Woods Hole Research Center, explains: "This is yet another example of the kind of slow-moving tropical systems that we expect to see more often as a response to climate change. Upper-level steering winds are slowing."[39] Professor Gabriel Vecchi of Princeton University agrees that Dorian "looks like what we're going to have more of in the future."[39] In September 2020, Hurricane Sally also stalled as it approached the coast.[40]

Another new phenomenon worsening tropical storms is the pools of abnormally hot water that randomly occur in the ocean.[41] Hurricane Florence immediately intensified after passing over a hot "blob" in the west-central Atlantic.[41] If hot "blobs" eventually accelerate ice melting at the poles, then sea levels may rise faster than anticipated.

Two studies were released in April 2022 that blamed climate change for ramping up extreme storms.[61] The first released study examined two intense tropical storms that struck southeastern Africa in early 2022. The second study examined the entire 2020 storm season, which included the record-breaking Atlantic hurricane season. This second study, published in the journal Nature Communications, also employed attribution science to compute numerical impacts of climate change.[61] Weather attribution science is explained in Chapter 5.

NOAA predictions for the 2022 hurricane season in the Atlantic Ocean expect "above normal" activity.[62] If so, that would make 2022 the seventh year in a row of above normal seasons.[62] Storm growth to hurricane strength (winds 74 mph or more) are expected to number 6-10, including 3-6 of Category 3 or greater. The odds of the 2022 hurricane season to be above normal activity were calculated to be a 65% chance.[62]

Rising Sea Levels

Approximately 600 million people live on the shores of Earth's oceans, directly exposed to rising seas.[42] Coastal flood plains are calculated to grow as much as another 100,000 square kilometers by 2100.[43] Damage to coastal cities could run 1 trillion dollars per year by 2050.[43] U.S. flood relief policy recently changed to moving homes to high ground rather than rebuild in place.[44] Recent high tide flooding along East and West coasts has been described as "extraordinary" by federal officials.[45] Frequent flooding in some cities has magnified by five times since the year 2000.[45]

Miami-Dade County recently released an "upbeat strategy" for coping with rising sea levels.[46] Various solutions offered included bringing in rock and dirt to hold back the seas. Other adaptation measures included building homes on stilts. But there were other voices for reducing carbon emissions in addition to adaptation strategies. Zelalem Adefris, Vice President of Catalyst Miami, observed, "We're not going to want to dredge and fill forever."[46] The seas are definitely rising, as is their rate of increase. The rate of increase in the last two decades is about double the average 20th-century rate.[47] The global mean sea level (GMSL) rate of rise over one century is now more than any century in the last 2,800 years, and is projected to continue increasing during the balance of this century.[4]

What causes the sea level increase? About 40% comes from thermal expansion of the ocean water, warmed by global warming.[48] A natural property of matter is to expand when heated (that is why bridges and concrete freeways are built with expansion joints to prevent buckling on hot days). Another one-third of sea level increase comes from mountain glacial runoff, which is ice and snow melted by global warming.[4] Chapter 1 provides extensive discussion of this phenomenon as physical proof that global warming is not a hoax. The rest of sea level rise is largely from melting ice at the poles primarily caused by ocean water heated by global warming. In other words, global warming is the principal cause of rising sea levels.

There is no doubt sea levels are steadily rising, but they are currently doing so rather slowly. Between 1993 and 2017, the total increase was under 9 centimeters, or about a 3.5 inches.[48] However, this increase does not seem small to island nations living close to the sea. Storms at sea send water surging over beaches and flooding coastal communities. Salt water intrusion on island soil is also a problem for underground freshwater supplies.[49] When Fiji, an island nation in the South Pacific, hosted the 2017 U.N. climate talks almost none of the measures to help them adapt to climate threats were resolved in those talks.[49] Prime Minister Gaston Browne of Antigua and Barbados opined, "The very thing that makes [Global North countries] wealthy is contributing to our vulnerability...It's only fair that they provide some level of compensation."[49] This kind of resentment is noted in Chapter 9 discussions of international climate talks. The economic vulnerability of poor nations to climate threats is analyzed in Chapter 4.

Cumulative additions to sea levels over the next 30 years are likely to flood many millions living near shorelines.[50.] For example, about one-fourth of Vietnam's population (20 million) is predicted to be inundated by 2050. Highly populated cities like Shanghai, Mumbai, Basra, and New Orleans will be largely underwater.[50] These estimates assume there are no significant surprises, such as abrupt releases of extraordinary ice masses into the sea surrounding Greenland and/or Antarctica. The National Climate Assessment (NCA) warns "both large–scale state shifts in the climate system (sometimes called ‘tipping points’) and compound extremes have the potential to generate unanticipated climate surprises."[4] With respect to sudden jumps in sea level originating from Antarctica, Chapter 1 explained the threat from the gigantic Thwaites Glacier, and Chapter 4 explained the new "sudden warming" threat to both West and East Antarctica. Those are known threats. Climate change is marked by uncertainties in uncharted situations (for which we lack historical records and comprehensive sensor measurements). What unknown sea-level threats are yet to be revealed?

Sudden, catastrophic jumps in sea level are quite possible in the not-too-distant future. The Thwaites Glacier in Antarctica, alone, could trigger a quick 11–foot jump in sea level, causing unexpected and profound devastation along all shorelines and shallow river deltas. That sea-level jump would be permanent (it would not retreat like a tsunami). After an 11-foot jump in sea level, future storm surges at high tide would be disastrous to communities having no history of such flooding.

There seems to be a tacit assumption that society will find a way to arrest global warming. The situation with melting ice at the poles is that some of this melting might already be unstoppable. If it is not already irreversible, it could become unstoppable as global warming continues. Society should understand that it could become unable to prevent the melting of all ice at the poles once tipping points have been breached. In that case, sea levels would eventually rise over 210 feet from current levels.

Such a flooding disaster to humanity and the biosphere challenges description. This would be an unintentional consequence of global warming, but the fact it was not intended would likely bring little comfort. Humankind has upset natural balances in the environment, and it risks certain consequences.

If global flooding is someday destined to reach over 200 feet above current sea levels, it would be rational for society to begin long-term adaptation preparations. Several centuries of such preparations might suffice. Those preparations could be designed to be consistent with society's ambitions for future development and progress. Thus, there should be no justification for panic or despair in contemplating a very distant flooding possibility.

Houses on Northern Carolina's Outer Banks are among recent victims of rising sea levels.[63] One home owner, Hiem Phan, watched an on-line video of his two story, four bedroom house topple into the sea and float away. "It's definitely a feeling you can't explain" he said, adding the feeling "is pretty empty".[63]

Outer Bank's beaches are shrinking fourteen feet per year in some locations. William Sweet, a sea level rise expert at NOAA explained that "waves are coming that much further inland, eating away at sand in a way that it would'nt if the seas were lower".[63]

Receding Mountain Glaciers

Two types of impacts are relevant: (1) impacts of global warming on mountain glaciers and (2) impacts of receding glaciers on society and the biosphere. Both types are discussed at length in Chapter 1, and its reading is recommended.

Receding mountain glaciers are included in this chapter not because they are an especially dangerous threat but, in context with other climate threats, their impact on fresh water availability could threaten the survival of humans and other life forms.

The sad fact is that global warming has partially or completely devastated at least 90% of Earth's mountain glaciers, and threatens their total extinction. Receding glaciers ultimately reduce fresh water supplies for human consumption, hydroelectric power generation, crop irrigation, and ecosystem survival (for example, fisheries). Global warming is degrading and eliminating an important asset in Earth's habitat. Receding mountain glaciers are also blemishing the natural beauty of Earth's environment and affecting resources for recreation and renewal.

Once Earth's mountain glaciers become extinct they will not likely return until another prolonged cooling trend or ice age. Chapter 1 provides a detailed account of the glacial retreat during this tragic loss.

* Note: Information sources are available in Chapter 1

Chapter 7 continues the description of climate threats.

Chapter 6 Sources

1. Rachel Nuwer, "Extinctions are Accelerating, Threatening Even Human Life," New York Times, June 3, 2020, p. A13 (I2840)
2. Kendra Pierre-Louis, "Bumblebees Feel the Deadly Sting of Climate Change," New York Times, February 11, 2020, p. D2 (I2792)
3. Palko Karasz, "Grim Signs of Climate Change in the Arctic: 200 Reindeer Dead of Starvation," New York Times, August 1, 2019, p. A4 (I2600)
4. Donald Wuebbles et al., "U.S. Global Change Research Program, Climate Science Special Report (CSSR)- National Climate Assessment," NOAA, June 28, 2017, pp. 1–669 (I2608)
5. Somini Sengupta, "Hotter Planet Already Poses Fatal Threats, Report Finds," New York Times, December 3, 2020, p. A15 (I2945)
6. Jana Benscoter, "Heat Stroke Tops List of Weather-Related Deaths", Patriot-News Pennlive, July 19, 2019, pp. 1-4 (I2671)
7. Christopher Flavelle, Nadja Popovich, "Heat-Related Deaths Rise in the Southwest as Temperatures Spike," New York Times, August 27, 2019, p. A13 (I2637)

8. John Schwartz, Nadja Popovich, "2018 Continues Warming Trend, as 4th Hottest Year Since 1880," New York Times, February 7, 2019, pp. 1, 19 (I2488)

9. Pamela Worth, "Killer Heat: Dangerously Hot Days Ahead," CATALYST (Union of Concerned Scientists), Summer 2019, pp. 8-12 (I2610)

10. Nadia Popovich, Blaki Migliozzi, "Dangerous Days: Your Hometown is Getting Hotter," New York Times, September 25, 2018, p. A16 (I2294)

11. Christopher Flavelle et. al., "New Data Reveals Hidden Flood Risks in U.S.," New York Times, June 30, 2020, p. A16 (I2848)

12. Damien Cave, "In Australia, Devastating Floods Are Part of The New Normal," New York Times, March 24, 2021, pp. 1, 19 (I3034)

13. Seth Borenstein, "Not Just Heat: Climate Change Can Be Seen all Around," The Seattle Times/Associated Press, June 14, 2018, p. A9 (I2232)

14. Tom DiLiberto, "River Flooding Inundates the Northern Plains in Spring 2019," NOAAClimate.gov, April 3, 2019, pp. 1-5 (I2672)

15. John Schwartz, "Heavy Rain, Catastrophic Floods and Complications of Climate Change," New York Times, March 23, 2019, p. A12 (I2514)

16. Christopher Flavelle, "Climate Change is Getting Worse, E.P.A. Says. Just Look Around," New York Times, May 13, 2021, pp.1, 21 (I3062)

17. Tom DiLiberto, "Flash Drought Engulfs the U.S. Southeast In September, 2019," NOAAClimate.gov., pp.1-5 (I2673)

18. Dan Nosowitz, "Extreme 'Flash Drought' Hits Farmers in the Southeast," Modern Farmer, October 7, 2019, pp. 1-3 (I2674)

19. Henry Fountain, "Southwest Drought Among Worst in Century," New York Times, April 17, 2020, p. A22 (2816)

20. John Schwartz, "Heat and Drought Team Up More Often to Ravage West," New York Times, September 24, 2020, p. A14 (I2905)

21. Henry Fountain, "In Southwest, Portent of 'Megadrought,'" New York Times, July 9, 2020, p. A14 (I2851)

22. John Schwartz, "More Floods and More Droughts: Climate Change Delivers Both," New York Times, December 12, 2018, pp. 1-4 (I2677)

23. John Schwartz, " 'Human 'Fingerprint' on Drought is Detected as Earth Warms," New York Times, May 2, 2019, p. A12 (I2533)

24. Staff, "Weekly Drought Map," NOAA Climate.gov, October 31, 2019, pp 1-2 (I2675)

25. Jonathan Overpeck, "Climate Change Is Increasing the Risk of Wildfires," World Economic Forum, November 29, 2018, pp. 1-6 (I2678)

26. AAAS Climate Panel, "What We Know" (about climate change), American Association for the Advancement of Science (AAAS), March 18, 2014, pp. 1-30 (I2085)

27. Carly Phillips, "Climate Change is Creating Catastrophic Wildfires," World Economic Forum, May 9, 2019, pp. 1-5 (I2679)

28. Staff, "Wildfires and Climate Change," Center for Climate and Energy Solutions, November 4, 2019, pp. 1-5 (I2680)

29. William Quarles, "Global Warming Means More Pathogens," IPM Practitioner, January, 2017, pp 1-5 (I2689)

30. Trip Gabriel, "Wildfires and Floods, But Little Talk of Climate Change by Candidates," New York Times, October 3, 2018, p. A24 (I2296)

31. Kendra Pierre-Louis "Complex Wildfire Grows in Ferocity as the Earth Heats," New York Times, August 29, 2019, pp. 1, 8 (I2640)

32. John Schwartz, Veronica Penney, "Giant Fires, Sparked by Lightning, 'That Can Start Anywhere,' " New York Times, October 24, 2020, p. 20 (I2912)

33. Kyle Dickman, "The Hidden Toll of Wildfire", Scientific American, March 2020, pp. 39-45 (I2804)

34. (repeat of source #31)

35. Staff, "Frequency Modulation," The Economist, September 2, 2017, pp.19-20 (I2113)

36. Kendra Pierre-Louis, "Storms Linger, Growing More Dangerous," New York Times, June 8, 2018, p. A15 (I2227)

37. Staff, "Stormy Weather," The Economist, September 22, 2018, pp. 54-55 (I2290)

38. Somini Sengupta, "Why Wilder Storms? It's a 'Loaded Dice' Problem," New York Times, October 6, 2018, p. A8 (I2430)

39. John Schwartz, "Mass of Clouds Provide Clearer View of Effects From Changing Climate," New York Times, September 4, 2019, p. A12 (I2606)

40. Henry Fountain, "A Warmer Earth is Leading to Slower, Wetter Hurricanes," New York Times, September 16, 2020, p.17 (I2895)

41. Jennifer Francis, "Rough Weather Ahead," Scientific American, June 2019, pp.46-53 (I2549)

42. Somini Sengupta, "Seas at the Front Door," New York Times, February 15, 2020, pp. A5-7 (I2795)

43. Staff, "A World Without Beaches," The Economist, September 17, 2019, pp. 11-12 (I2622)

44. Christopher Flavelle, "U.S. Flood Relief Shifts to Moving Homes to Safety," New York Times, August 27, 2020, pp.1, 20 (I2883)

45. Christopher Flavelle, "Data Show an 'Extraordinary' Rise in Coastal Flooding," New York Times, July 15, 2020, p. A19 (I2853)

46. Christopher Flavelle, Patricia Mazzei, "Miami Says it Can Adapt As Seas Rise. Not Everyone is Convinced," New York Times, March 3, 2021, p.A12 (I3024)

47. (repeat of source#26)

48. Staff, "Higher Tide," The Economist, August 17, 2019, pp.15-18 (I2623)

49. Brad Plumer, Lisa Friedman, "Island Leaders Losing Hope in U.N. Climate Talks," New York Times, November 18, 2017, p. A5 (I2152)

50. Denise Lu, Christopher Flavelle, "Erased by Rising Seas By 2050," New York Times, October 30, 2019, p. A6 (I2684)

51. Bhadra Sharma, Mike Ives, "Waters Rise Across South Asia, Causing Dozens of Deaths in Region," New York Times, July 16, 2019, p. A7 (I2587)

52. Binyamin Appelbaum, "Enough About Climate Change. Air Pollution is Killing Us Now", New York Times, April 30, 2022, p. A22 (I3158)

53. Henry Fountain, "Climate Change Doubled Odds of April's Deadly Floods in South Africa, Study Says", New York Times, May 14, 2022, p. A4 (I3164)

54. Henry Fountain, "Western Drought is the Worst in 1,200 Years", New York Times, February 15, 2022, p. A12 (I3135)

55. Henry Fountain, "Expecting Western Drought to End Soon? Not Likely, Forecasters Say", New York Times, February 18, 2022, p. A20 (I3136)

56. Andrew Schwartz, "California's Drought is Worse Than We Thought", New York Times, April 5, 2022, p. A23 (I3150)

57. Raymond Zhong, "Climate Change Raises Risk of Major Wildfires", New York Times, February 23, 2022, February 23, 2022, p. A6 (I3137)

58. Chelsea Harvey, "Wildfires Could Transform Amazon from Carbon Sink to Source" Scientific American (E&E News), January 14, 2020, pp. 1-6 (I3114).

59. Simon Romero, "Largest Wildfire in New Mexico's History is One of Many Scorching the Southwest", New York Times, May 23, 2022, p. A17 (I3167)

60. Christopher Flavelle, "Wildfire Risks to U.S. Homes Grow Greater" New York Times, May 17, 2022, pp. 1,17 (I3166)

61. Maggie Astor, "Record-Setting Hurricane Season Was Wetter Because of Climate Change", New York Times, April 13, 2022, p. A17 (I3154)

62. Maggie Astor, "NOAA is Predicting Another Busy Hurricane Season", New York Times, May 25, 2022, p. A21 (I3169)

63. Richard Fausset, "Beach Houses on the Outer Banks Are Being Swallowed by the Sea", New York Times, May 16, 2022, p. A15 (I3165)

Chapter 7: Climate Threats, Part Two

The climate threats discussed in Part Two are:

Microbes and disease threats

Deforestation: a dire past and future

Global economic threats

Threats to the biosphere and biodiversity

Marine carbon reservoirs

These Part Two threats can be somewhat more involved than those in Part One, and they warrant more in-depth discussion. This is especially true for the deforestation topic. The economic topic is close behind in substantive depth.

Microbes and Disease Threats

Chapter 4 related a story about how toxic septic tank fluids migrated to contaminate ocean beaches and infect swimmers with various ailments. This story illustrated interesting climate dynamics, but it also revealed a general problem with global warming impacts. When the environment warms, it can also enhance conditions for disease amplification and propagation.[1] For instance, record temperatures in the U.S. pushed COVID-19 case counts higher and made it more difficult to protect people at higher risk.[2] A Harvard study also confirmed virus deaths are linked to fine-particle air pollution, including that associated with climate change.[3] Climate change also has a role in making it easier for pathogenic microbes to cause disease[4] An example is the migration of deadly fungi like *Candida auris* and *Aspergillus* beyond traditional boundaries. Such fungal diseases infect about 300 million people and kill 1.6 million each year worldwide—more than malaria.[5]

The public would be wise to heed the warnings of microbiologists, such as Professor Rick Cavicchioli of the University of New South Wales. He led an initiative by 30 microbiologists from 9 countries to publish a climate change warning in the journal Nature Reviews Microbiology (June 18, 2019). The purpose of this warning initiative was to inform readers of "how microbes can influence climate change and how they will be impacted by it."[4.] Professor Cavicchioli elaborated: "Micro-organisms, which include bacteria and viruses, are the lifeforms that you don't see on the conservation websites. They support the existence of all higher lifeforms and are critically important in regulating climate change."[4] He further noted: "Climate change also expands the number and geographic range of vectors (such as mosquitoes) that carry pathogens. The end result is the increased spread of disease, and serious threats to global food supplies."[4.]

Although environmental media seems to lack focus on the microbe aspect of global warming threat, this author found keen interest in other media, including WebMD, The IPM Practitioner (monitoring the field of pest management) and World Economic Forum. This "alternate" media would likely agree with the thrust of the Cavicchioli initiative discussed above. Discussion continues, based primarily on these "alternate" media sources.

New studies indicate climate change is "at least partially responsible" for the 2015 Zika virus epidemic that infected half a million people in 40 countries.[6] Jonathan Patz, MD, Director, Global Health Institute (University of Wisconsin, Madison) commented: "The climate conditions were very high risk for having Zika transmission."[6] Ashish Jha, MD, (Director, Harvard Global Health Institute) commented at a "Climate and Health" conference at the Carter Center in Atlanta: "As the climate changes, so will infectious diseases we confront. More outbreaks like Ebola and Zika. More pandemics like the bird flu..."[6]

Human diseases increasing in frequency and geographic extent in recent decades include malaria, yellow fever, dengue, Lyme disease, and tick-borne encephalitis.[7.] Mosquitoes and ticks, thriving on warmth and moisture, carry these diseases.[7] Small outbreaks in malaria have occurred in

New York, New Jersey, Michigan, Florida, Georgia, and Texas since 1990.[7] It should be noted that extreme conditions caused by global warming, such as flooding and drought, are favored for mosquito breeding.[7]

An exotic aspect of the microbe threat in a warming environment is the thawing of frozen soil, which can then release ancient microbes.[8] An actual case has been recorded of anthrax spores released from a thawed reindeer carcass in Siberia. Alexei Kokorin of WWF Russia reports that permafrost thawing in Russia is occurring in cemeteries, animal burial grounds, and along river banks where nomads were known for burying their dead.[8.]

Before closing this discussion on microbes and disease, a broad overview on this climate threat might be helpful. Big factors in disease propagation are the land-use squeeze and habitat loss that bring people and disease into closer contact.[9] Another factor is species extinction that introduces diseases into new hosts.[9] A third factor is climate-driven migrations that introduce diseases to new populations. Examples include migrations of tropical diseases to moderate climates and migrations to escape intense heat and drought.[9]

A new study published in late April 2022 determined that climate change is increasing the pace of disease spread between species.[70] Global warming is forcing species to seek cooler habitats. As they move to higher altitudes or higher latitudes they encounter different species, meaning more opportunities for interspecies disease spread. This also means greater odds for humans to be infected by pathogens.

Two studies released in February 2022 concluded Covid-19 emerged under a climate change scenario approximating the one described above.[70] The virus jumped from bats to wild animals being sold in a Wuhan market. Humans were next in line and an extremely deadly pandemic followed.

The April study examined 3,139 species and computed 4,000 opportunities for virus jumps would result from the greater frequency of different species encounters.[70] Co-author of the study Gregory Albery (Georgetown University disease ecologist): "We believe that (virus spread) is something that could happen a lot as a result of the ----- transmission events that we are predicting".[70]

The threat outlook is not good. For example, COVID-19 and its variants have proven to be more dangerous and damaging than first thought. Imagine two or three simultaneous pandemics, each more dangerous and damaging than COVID-19. That might be what the future holds if forces behind disease escalation are not arrested. Other climate threats might pale in the shadow of galloping diseases ravaging Earth's peoples.

Deforestation: A Dire Past and Future

Deforestation is a cousin to global warming because removal of CO_2 sinks has the end result of adding more CO_2 to the atmosphere. Also, deforestation by wildfires adds heat and CO_2 directly to the atmosphere.[10] Atmospheric warming removes moisture from the forest, allowing fires to burn intensely and out of control. Climate change has likely increased the frequency and intensity of droughts, which leave the forests tinder dry for the next wildfire. In summary, deforestation and global warming make each other worse.

Actual reduction of pollution in the future will require reversals of both global warming and deforestation. This is easier said than done. Deforestation and global warming are both highly muddled issues. It should be mentioned that nature is a principal cause of deforestation. Nature's agents include beavers, forest diseases, pests, droughts, lightning-caused wildfires, and (of course) human beings.

Deforestation is as old as civilization itself. Living trees became dugout canoes and footbridges over creeks and streams. Forests were cleared to make way for villages and pathways between villages. The Agricultural Revolution in the first millennium A.D. witnessed large forest areas being cleared to accommodate expanding farms. The second millennium A.D. brought a much-expanded population and the Industrial Revolution. Forests were cleared for expanding cities and suburbs, interconnecting roads and railways, and industrial parks. Forests were also cleared to harvest wood pulp for making paper products. By the dawn of the third millennium A.D., deforestation had devastated most of the world's primary-growth forests, plus many of the secondary- and tertiary-growth ones. Rainforest devastation and the long cultural tradition of giving development priority over conservation are contemporary concerns.

These preliminary remarks should begin to help readers understand the convoluted deforestation issue. Think of it as a tug-of-war between those who value development over conservation and those who value conservation over development. It is not quite that simple, but this is a rough approximation. Complicating factors include national sovereignty, individual rights, poverty, tipping points, and unenforceable law. It is truly a "can of worms." One should not expect a clear, simple solution to deforestation. There is likely none.

Deforestation is happening throughout the planet due to wildfires, intentionally set fires, logging and land clearing. Rainforest losses are grabbing the greatest attention recently but wildfires can happen most anywhere, such as California, Alaska and Siberia.[11] Peat, a dirt-like material, is also burning in Arctic regions now that global warming has evaporated much of the moisture that had previously prevented peat fires.[11.] Burning peat releases much more CO_2 than burning trees do.

Rainforests throughout the tropics are losing tree cover, as proven by statistics compiled by Global Forest Watch (Mongabay). Between 2001 and 2008 Brazil, Indonesia, and Democratic Republic of Congo have lost the following amounts of tree cover:

Brazil	198,915 square miles
Indonesia	96,395 square miles
DR Congo	49,549 square miles

The 18-year tree-cover loss in Brazil alone is greater than the combined areas of Alabama, Georgia, Florida, and South Carolina. Hundreds of fires in Indonesia (Borneo and Sumatra) burned in mid-September 2019.[10] About

80% were set to clear land for palm crops, but many burned out of control due to poorly equipped firefighters.[10] Officials counted 2,900 hotspots throughout the country, including Papau Province, Java, and Sulawesi. The thick smoke sickened thousands and interfered with air travel.[10] Extensive peatlands were burning with the forests. President Joko Widodo urged that fires not be set and the Indonesian government shut down over two dozen plantations where fires were spotted.[10]

Rainforests are also ablaze in Central Africa and sections of Southern Africa during the dry season. The Congo River basin rainforest is the second-largest in the world (after the Amazon).[12] The Congo lost about 6% of its rainforest (or 13 million hectares) between 2001 and 2018—an area double that of Ireland.[13] Out-of-control fires are made more likely by rising temperatures, decreased rainfall, and logging practices. Also, regional governments in Africa are lacking technical and financial resources to fight fires (compared to South American countries). Forest manager Irene Wabiwa Betoko says, "If [fire] catches the rainforest in the Congo basin, it will be worse than in South America."[12]

Brazil's National Institute for Space Research is able to monitor fires using satellite images. In August 2019, it reported detecting 74,155 fires in the Amazon rainforest—an 84% increase over the same period in 2018.[14] The loss of wetlands in Brazil set a record in 2020.[15] Ane Alencar, Science Director, Amazon Environmental Research Institute (Brazil) was concerned because "[w]e are at the beginning of the fire season. This could still get much worse."[14]

The Amazon basin, home to 40% of the world's rainforests, lies mostly in Brazil, but its boundaries also intersect Bolivia, Peru, Ecuador, Colombia and Venezuela.[16] Colombia is opening jungle land to settlers -- illegal gold mining and cocoa farming are behind rainforest losses in Peru --- and Bolivian ranchers are clearing rainforests to raise beef for the Chinese market.[17] Brazil alone lost 1,330 square miles of forest cover in 7 months (Jan–July 2019)—a 39% increase over the same period in 2018.[18]

How much rainforest loss can the Amazon Basin sustain before reaching a catastrophic tipping point? That is a growing concern.[16, 19, 20, 21, 22] A related question is: How close is the Amazon basin to its tipping point? Some say "may be perilously close."[19] One quantified estimate is 20–25% deforestation.[20] Others call it "imminent" and define the situation after tipping as self-perpetuating deforestation also known as "dieback." As the dieback continues, the rainforest could transform into savanna.[20.] During dieback, decomposition would be releasing stored carbon into the air.[23] Plant life in the Amazon is estimated to store 100 billion tons of carbon.[24] The great carbon sink would then become a great carbon emitter—with two-fold impact![71]

The tipping point threat results from gradual degradation of the rainforest. Ben Hur Marimon of the University of Mato Grosso explains they see "two warmings in one." In addition to global warming, deforestation robs the forest of the cooling effect via water evaporation from trees' leaves.[16] Marimon further remarks that trees begin to dry out at temperatures above 40°C, and become more likely to be dropped by strong winds. Also, farming fragments the forest, making access to water and seed banks a challenge to recover.[16] Land clearing leads to local drying, which reduces rainfall. A 2012 study at the University of Leeds forecasted that by 2050, Amazon rainfall would drop 12% in the wet season and 21% in the dry season.[16]

There are two prominent theories on what will happen to the Amazon forest after it passes the tipping point.[20] The first scenario maintains that dieback devastation will be limited only to the most severely damaged forest regions. The second scenario maintains the Amazon's weather pattern would be so disrupted that the Basin's rainforest could be transformed into savanna. No one knows whether the pessimistic scenario is even possible.[20] Scientists believe the dieback cycle could be stopped if caught early.[20] The trick might be detecting when the dieback cycle starts and promptly instituting policies and amassing resources to stop the cycle. If this can be done, it should be done now, as a preemptive measure.

Brazil has lost 17% of its rainforest in the last 50 years. The losses are due primarily to infrastructure development (such as roads and dams), mining, logging, cattle ranching, and soya bean farming.[19] Law enforcement has been a recurring challenge. Brazil's recently elected president, Jair Bolsonaro, has made it clear lawbreakers need not watch their backs. Logging is 70%–80% illegal but the virtual absence of law enforcement has encouraged record-breaking deforestation.[19] Pessimists fear a catastrophic tipping point would be triggered with 3–8% further deforestation. That fear is buttressed by the fact the Amazon has suffered three severe droughts in the last 15 years.[19] President Bolsonaro dismisses such talk, and accuses rich countries of using environmental dogma to keep Brazil poor. "The Amazon is ours," he declares. However, Brazil is also a victim of deforestation. The 2015 drought caused farmers in Central Brazil to lose one-third of their corn crop.[19] Brazil might also face foreign boycotts if deforestation continues unchecked.[19].

How do farmers and miners in the Amazon Basin feel about deforestation and international concerns? Many believe it is their right to do as they please with their personal property, and outsiders should mind their own business.[25] In other words, they feel much the same way as their peers on the planet! Texans, for example, are generally proud of their reputation for similar attitudes. "Don't mess with Texas" is a familiar expression. Amazonians don't want to be messed with either.

There is global outrage over decimation of rainforests that provide 20% of the world's oxygen, and whose preservation is vital to combating climate change.[26] The actor Leonardo DiCaprio has asserted that "the lungs of the Earth are in flames" and urged his more than 33 million Instagram followers to be aware of the deforestation situation.[26] However, Brazil's President Bolsonaro has shot back at Western critics and news media, claiming they are intentionally misleading the public. Filipe Martins, policy advisor to President Bolsonaro, has also responded to international criticism: "There's a reason why Brazil has the best environmental credentials and the best preserved forests...We know how to protect and take care of what is ours."[27] Brazilian Jeronimo Goergen, a federal lawmaker, has expressed concerns about the deforestation debate: "This creates a terrible image for Brazil...The agricultural sector stands to suffer the most based on the way this debate is being framed."[26]

Down on the farm, Agamenon da Silva Menezes wonders what all the fuss is about. He is a farmer's union leader in northern Brazil who claims fires are the normal way to clear land for crops and the dry season is the natural time to do the clearing.[25] In an interview, he explained: "We're going to continue producing here in the Amazon and we're going to continue feeding the world...There's no need for all this outrage."[25]

Beginning in about 1980, the Amazon rainforest began losing significant acreage and continuity. In a region of widespread poverty and unemployment, making use of the forest was a way to survive and afford a better life.[25] Logging, mining, farming, raising cattle, and selling property were the means.[25] Professor Mauricio Torres of the Federal University of Pará noted: "The land is made 50, 100, 200 times as valuable once it has been deforested. It's an excellent business..."[25]

At the turn of the century, the Brazilian government implemented a plan to cut the rate of deforestation. However, the plan depended on effective law enforcement. It worked well for a while, but a deep economic recession, increased economic dependence on agriculture, and migration deep into the forest made environmental law enforcement less popular and less practical. The strict rules became perceived as a drag on the economy.[25] Law enforcement was relaxed and deforestation regained momentum. The election of Mr. Bolsonaro brought greater priority on development than on conservation. Environmental law enforcement became increasingly impotent. The federal environmental agency was warned recently by a prosecutor that a group was planning to set fires along a major arterial. Agency officials replied they did not have sufficient resources to stop the arsonists.[25]

Relations between Brazil and the international community could be described as quirky at times. At a recent G7 meeting, world leaders pledged over $22 million to help fight the Amazon rainforest fires.[28] This offer was angrily rejected by Brazil's government and the G7 was told to mind its own business. However, the next day, President Bolsonaro suggested possible terms of aid acceptance, provided Mr. Macron, president of France, withdrew insults and insinuations that Brazil did not have sovereignty over the Amazon.[28] Bolsonaro said, "He will have to withdraw his words, and then we can talk."[28] During a meeting with his cabinet and governors from all nine states in the Amazon Basin, the deforestation crisis was discussed. Mr. Bolsonaro claimed the international demonstrations were attempting to infringe on Brazil's territorial rights: "What they want is our sovereignty...We have to unite to preserve what is ours and guarantee our sovereignty."[28] When President Biden recently hinted at consequences if Brazil did not "stop tearing down the rainforest," Mr. Bolsonaro responded in a tweet, "OUR SOVEREIGNTY IS NON-NEGOTIABLE."[29]

The international community has been showing signs of increased agitation over the Amazon rainforest situation. Norway and Germany have suspended contributions to the Amazon Fund, which supports environmental law enforcement. A major trade deal between Europe and four South American countries (including Brazil) has yet to be ratified.[28] Brazilian Blairo Maggi, a former culture minister and principal shareholder of an important trading group, recently expressed concern that the deforestation crisis could precipitate a boycott of Brazil's exports.[28]

There is no shortage of good reasons to halt deforestation. In its June 2020 issue, the editors of Scientific American made a compelling case that wild habitat must be preserved to prevent pandemics from becoming commonplace and spawning novel strains.[30]

Five factors complicating the resolution of the deforestation crisis were noted earlier: national sovereignty, individual rights, poverty, tipping points, and unenforceable law. Each factor has been noted in the above discussion. The passage of time might help unravel these complications, but the tipping point threat suggests that rainforests may already be on the brink of dieback catastrophe.

As noted in Chapter 2, the rate of deforestation and loss of carbon sinks is increasing rapidly. Is time for unraveling complex issues and avoiding a tipping point about to run out? A report released in late 2021[72] should cause alarm. Deforestation in the Amazon grew at the fastest pace in the last 15 years.[72] Between August 2020 and July 2021, 5,100 square miles of prime rainforest were lost in the Amazon alone.

An April 2022 report from the World Resources Institute found the 2021 old growth rainforest loss worldwide totaled 9.3 million acres (over 14,000 square miles).[73] Global tropical forest loss totaled 27 million acres (over 42,000 square miles) in 2021.

Pledges made at the U.N. climate summit in Glasgow (November 2021) to "halt and reverse" deforestation by 2030 will require drastic action, according to Frances Seymour of the World Resources Institute.[73] But is 2030 too late to prevent a feared tipping point where the deforestation process becomes irreversible? No one can know the numerical risk with certainty, but the risk is certain. Society should consider ramping up managing the deforestation situation as it did successfully in managing the "ozone hole" crisis.

This completes the current assessment of the deforestation situation. Chapter 12 speaks to both short-term and long-term possibilities. Perhaps those all should be short term.

Global Economic Threats

Introduction

As this book is nearing publication, there are a number of recent events indicating growing interest in climate threats to the global economy. Concerns that these economic threats are seriously underestimated are likewise growing. This latter concern was the subject of an authoritative study by three groups of scientists and economists: the London School of Economics and Political Science; the Potsdam Institute for Climate Impact Research; and Columbia University's Earth Institute.[31] One fundamental reason for economic threat underestimation is that the pace and severity of climate change has been underestimated.[31.] But there are other fundamental reasons, largely due to how economists normally gauge economic risks. First, they historically depend on "stationary, experience-defined risk—which is incompatible with a continually evolving climate situation." Second, risks that are not easily quantified tend to be omitted from economic threat assessment. Third, economic risks are usually gauged for singular situations and dynamic, interactive and cascading situations do not fit economic models. (The study report provides examples of these risk assessment limitations). For these reasons, it is believed the probable economic threat from climate change is much greater than is currently anticipated. Consequently, "neither the magnitude of the risks to lives and livelihoods nor the urgency of action" are widely understood.[31]

Climate threats to the global economy are causing concern in high places. Federal regulators commissioned a report to assess the situation, which concluded: "A world wracked by frequent and devastating shocks from climate change cannot sustain the fundamental conditions supporting our financial system."[32] More specifically they worry about financial markets as disaster costs "spread through insurance and mortgage markets, pension funds and other financial institutions.[32]

Perhaps the kind of situation that might cause market jitters is one in which economically vulnerable nations are faced with rising climate costs. There are more than a few nations caught between the crisis of unsustainable debt and the climate change crisis.[33] This situation has caught the attention of the IMF and World Bank, which recently stated that it "represents a systemic risk to the global economy that might trigger a cycle that depresses revenues, increases spending and exacerbates climate and nature vulnerabilities."[33]

In February 2020, the Group of 20 finance ministers adopted a statement that "financial stability implications of climate change" were to be monitored.[34]

The rising costs of climate disasters are part of the economic threat. In 2019, there were 14 climate disasters costing at least 1 billion dollars each—the fifth year in a row of 10 or more such disasters.[35] The National Oceanic and Atmospheric Administration (NOAA) has warned climate change is increasing the frequency and costs of extreme weather events.[35.] In the fall of 2017, the U.S. Congress' Government Accountability Office issued a study report warning of rising climate change costs.[36] In a separate report, a White House calculation estimated the federal government had spent $350 billion over the past decade to aid victims of extreme weather.[36]

In 2017, there were 16 extreme weather events (hurricanes, etc.) each costing at least 1 billion dollars in losses.[37] This compares to only 3 disasters in 1980 costing over $1 billion each (adjusted for inflation). The 2017 total for all extreme weather events was $306 billion.[37] This includes $120 billion for Hurricane Harvey, $90 billion for Hurricane Maria, and $50 billion for Hurricane Irma. The western U.S. wildfires and firestorms cost $18 billion.[37]

These major hurricanes in 2017 demonstrated the propagation of destructive impacts through interconnected economic sectors.[38] For example, Harvey's power outages affected wastewater treatment plants and hospitals. Interruption of oil production and refining in the Gulf of Mexico caused both regional and national price spikes.[38.] Hurricanes Maria and Irma also affected the agricultural industry.

Unrelated to hurricanes, the 2011 Missouri River flood caused a nuclear power plant (near Omaha, Nebraska) to shut down and remain out of service for years.[39.] More recent flooding in Nebraska occurred during record-breaking floods in the Midwest in March 2019. That flooding was aggravated by a dam failure in northern Nebraska that washed out roads and rail lines important to farmers for carrying crops to market.[40] It was bad timing for a massive natural disaster, given that Chapter 12 bankruptcy filings in the Midwest had risen 19% in 2018. Climate disasters are literally driving farmers out of business.[40]

The opposite of too much water is too little water. Droughts can also have devastating economic impacts, as illustrated by the commercial consequences of low river levels in Europe in the fall of 2018. Three major rivers in Germany—the Rhine, the Danube, and the Elbe—were at such low levels that commercial traffic was highly restricted.[41] Gas stations ran out of fuel because tankers from refineries in the Netherlands were sidelined. Germany's ferry traffic was cut in half. Cruise ships had to offload passengers for bus transport on parts of their river itineraries. Thousands of fish died because of high water temperatures and low oxygen levels. The Rhine alone transports 80% of Germany's 223 million tons of annual ship-borne cargo. One reason for the Rhine's low water level was that the Alps' snow and glacier reserves had been reduced by climate change.[41]

Is climate change also affecting economics in the Alps? The answer is a definite yes, because the tourist industry is taking a big hit from shortened winter sports seasons and less low-elevation snow.[43] The Alps have warmed by 2°C. Worldwide winter sports are also experiencing economic losses similar to those in the Alps.[43] A 100-day ski season is usually needed to turn a profit. A 2007 study estimated that about 40% of 666 Alpine ski resorts can no longer rely on 100-day seasons.[43]

A fierce drought in the western U.S. has been underway since 2000, and is feared to become a "megadrought" of historic proportions.[42] Ranchers in North Dakota are hauling water for livestock. California, Arizona, and New Mexico each have multiple wildfires out of control. Utah is among those states in an extreme drought category.[42] It seems no one in the western U.S. will escape this economic and climate disaster that continues to unfold.

The economic costs of climate change do not always affect large geographic areas and multiple economic sectors—they can be laser-focused on a single industry in a limited region. When Europe suffered a heat wave in 2017, an economic victim was the olive oil industry in the foothills of central Italy.[44] Flowers on the olive trees were literally withering in the unseasonal spring heat, and there was precious little water to irrigate the parched orchards. Climate change in that region is making olive oil a risky livelihood.[44] One producer predicted 60% less yield than normal.

Economic disasters from weather extremes can even be laser-focused on a single corporation. The Pacific Gas & Electric Company (PG&E), serving 16 million Californians, was valued at $25 billion before the catastrophic Camp Fire devastated Paradise, California.[45] PG&E has now filed for bankruptcy because it apparently did not do enough to prevent wildfires (many of which were caused by downed power lines).[45] The message to be taken from this episode is that businesses need to evaluate climate risks and take appropriate action.

Current Trends

"Earth's climate is now changing faster than at any point in the history of modern civilization," according to the November 2018 Fourth National Climate Assessment Overview.[38] For example, higher temperatures are causing droughts to intensify and adding urgency to conservation.[38] Current climate mitigation and adaptation efforts are insufficient "to avoid substantial damages to the U.S. economy."[38] Climate change impacts to the economy are growing and with that climate-related threats are intensifying.[38] Also, multiple climate disasters are occurring in many places, resulting in a compounding of risks.[38] Regional economies are more vulnerable to climate change impacts.[38] For example, electrical power generation and distribution are at greater risk to weather extremes.[38] Oil and gas operations in Alaska are affected by sea level rise and thawing permafrost. Agriculture is faced with extreme rainfall, increasing drought, range wildfires and reduced productivity during heat waves.[38] Federal programs to assist farmers with climate costs stalled in late 2018 because the farm bill in Congress had expired.[39]

Costs of climate change are being taken seriously by industries most affected by climate disasters.[45] Measures to reduce climate impacts, called climate adaptation, are being implemented in anticipation of worsening weather ahead. Electric utilities are working to protect the grid infrastructure, and the transportation sector is hardening port facilities and rail lines to withstand wildfires and floods.[45] Many realize the importance of reducing carbon emissions to limit future warming.[45] "Business is no longer business as usual" in the opinion of R. Mukundan, chief executive of

Tata Chemicals, located in Mumbai, India (which has experienced extreme flooding).[46] One asset survey of 11,000 global companies estimated climate risks could reach as high as 20% losses in value. Rating agencies are beginning to include physical climate risk in establishing corporate scores.[46]

One way companies are adapting to new climate realities is by seeking protection by purchasing insurance policies.[47.] Worldwide casualty insurance premiums totaled $2.4 trillion in 2018.[47] Annual insurance losses have climbed 20 times since the 1970s and averaged $65 billion this decade (adjusted for inflation). The gap between total losses and insured losses grew to $1.2 trillion in the 18-year period following the year 2000.[47] According to insurers, adaptation measures like installing flood barriers around factories and reinforcing warehouse roofs to withstand stronger gusts are highly cost-effective. One dollar spent on adaptation can save five dollars in reconstruction.[48.]

Future Economic Impacts

The Fourth National Climate Assessment (Summary Findings) summarized future economic impacts of climate change as follows:[49] "[T]he continued warming that is projected to occur without substantial and sustained reductions in global greenhouse gas emissions is expected to cause substantial net damage to the U.S. economy throughout this century, especially in the absence of increased adaptation efforts. With continued growth in emissions at historic rates, annual losses in some economic sectors are projected to reach billions of dollars by the end of the century—more than the current gross domestic product (GDP) of many U.S. states."

Note the phrase "substantial and sustained reductions in global greenhouse gas emissions" (global is underlined for emphasis). In other words, the fate of the U.S. economy depends on global behavior.

The Fourth National Climate Assessment (overview) remarked that "climate-related risks will continue to grow without additional action. Decisions made today determine risk exposure for current and future generations..." [38] Referring specifically to economic impacts, this climate assessment asserted: "Without more significant global greenhouse gas mitigation and regional adaptation efforts, climate change is expected to cause substantial losses to infrastructure and property and impede the rate of economic growth over the century."[38] ("Global" is underlined for emphasis.) This official climate assessment (mandated by Congress) also noted climate impacts overseas will affect U.S. businesses that have international operations and supply chains. Import and export prices could also be affected by overseas climate disasters.[38] Extreme weather events are expected to be both more intense and more frequent and effects of damaged infrastructure "can cascade across economic sectors."[38] Massive power outages and fuel shortages would have broad economic impacts, including increased costs of damage recovery.

Rising sea levels will put U.S. coastal infrastructure and other federal assets valued at $1 trillion at risk. Devastation of critical transportation infrastructure "is expected to result in cascading costs and national impacts."[38.] Oil, natural gas, and electrical power facilities are exposed to both sea level rise and hurricanes along the Gulf of Mexico and Atlantic oceans. Destruction of those facilities is expected to have negative effects on both the regional and national economy.[38]

Rising temperatures in the western U.S. and the Midwest are expected to increase extreme weather losses. Wildfires in the west will be aggravated by drier conditions and result in greater losses of property and infrastructure.[38.] Dry conditions in the Midwest will intensify drought conditions and slash crop yields. Also, higher temperatures during the growing season are expected to be the most important reason for reduced agricultural productivity.[38] By 2090 extreme heat could cause the loss of some two billion labor hours annually, which converts to "costing an estimated $160 billion" in reduced paychecks nation-wide.[38]

Global temperatures continue to rise, but a significant unknown is how much they will rise this century: A 2017 study at the University of California, Berkeley found economic impacts rise sharply with temperature increases.[50] U.S. economic performance is measurably impaired with slight temperature increases. U.S. output could fall up to 1.7% with a 1.5°C global increase (compared to pre-industrial temperatures). A 4 degree increase could drop economic output by as much as 5.6% GNP.[50] However, in "worst-case" scenarios, global temperatures could increase 5°C.[51] A carbon emissions surge (discussed in Chapter 2) could push temperatures still higher.

"Worst case" is placed in quotes because a key assumption in the scenario is future rates of temperature increase will be no worse than the current rate.[51] There are at least two reasons why this assumption will prove false. First, global demand for fossil fuels is forecasted to rise sharply this century (see Chapter 2). Second, the possibility of tipping point surprises in future climate change cannot be excluded.[51] For example, wildfire intensification, accelerated deforestation, and/or permafrost thawing could cause a large and unexpected increase in greenhouse gas concentration in the atmosphere. In other words, global temperature increases might top out significantly higher than 5°C this century. One result of higher-than-anticipated global temperatures would be underestimated economic impacts.

An additional possibility for underestimated economic impacts is tipping point events that accelerate sea level rises (see Chapter 4). Such events might include instantaneous jumps in sea level, which would have catastrophic economic consequences worldwide, not to mention causing unprecedented loss of life.

Threats to the Biosphere and Biodiversity

First, some fundamentals. The biosphere is the sole habitat for all Earth's life forms, including humans. This shared environment supports all life forms, and the welfare of all is interdependent. An unhealthy habitat can lead to the extinction of species, including humans. Maintenance of species diversity is helpful to the survival and wellbeing of all life forms. Humans are the only species capable of monitoring and preserving Earth's biosphere.

Evidence concerning the current state of Earth's biosphere was established by a United Nation's report released in mid-2019. This 1500-

page document, prepared by hundreds of scientists, was based on thousands of scientific studies.[52] It concluded human-caused changes to the biosphere have put 1 million plant and animal species at risk.[52] This biosphere assessment was conducted by Intergovernmental Science—Policy on Biodiversity and Ecosystems Services (IPBES). The chair of this organization, Sir Robert Watson, commented: "For a long time people just thought of biodiversity as saving nature for its own sake...But this report makes clear the links between biodiversity and nature and things like food security and clean water in both rich and poor countries."[52] He further warned: "The health of ecosystems on which we and all other species depend is deteriorating more rapidly than ever. We are eroding the very foundations of our economies, livelihood, food security, health and quality of life worldwide."[53]

The IPBES report, titled IPBES Global Assessment, contains a wealth of information that defines the current state of biodiversity/habitat deterioration. This report was three years in the making, and it represents one of the most comprehensive and authentic compilations of its kind. Examples of relevant information from the IPBES report are listed below to help convey the scope and gravity of biodiversity/habitat decline:[53.]

1. 85%of wetlands present in 1700 were gone by 2000. Percentage-wise, wetland loss is currently three times faster than rate of deforestation.

2. The current rate of global species extinction is accelerating, and it is 10–100 times faster than the average rate over the last 10 million years.

3. Over 40% of amphibian species are at risk of extinction.

4. Twenty-three percent of land area has reduced productivity.

5. Thirty-three percent of marine stocks were overfished in 2015.

6. Four hundred low-oxygen "dead zones" in coastal ecosystems (caused by fertilizer runoff) affect over 245,000 km^2.

7. Today's global forest area is 68% of its estimated pre-industrial level. Two hundred and ninety million hectares of native forests were harvested during the 1990–2015 period.

8. Over 800 million people in Asia and Africa face food shortages.

9. Over 80% of global wastewater is discharged into the environment without treatment.

10. Greenhouse gas emissions have doubled since 1980.

11. Tourism's carbon footprint increased 40% from 2009 to 2013, releasing 4.5 Gtons of carbon dioxide.

12. Forty percent of the global population lacks access to clean and safe drinking water.

Another example of biosphere degradation that concerns scientists is the decline of wild bees and insects that pollinate crops. At risk is $577 billion worth of annual crop production. A second example is the loss of flood protection provided by coral reefs and mangrove forests. It is estimated this loss exposes 300 million people to increased risk of flooding.[52]

Climate change impacts on planet life are alarming—plant and animal abundance has declined 20% or more, mostly during the 20th century. Biodiversity loss is expected to accelerate until at least 2050 if nations fail to make aggressive steps to improve conservation. The authors of the IPBES report expressed the need for greater conservation priority over economic development.[52] Emma Archer (who led an earlier assessment of Africa's biodiversity) made the point that if the value of what protected nature provides is not considered, "then ultimately human well-being will be compromised."[52] Scientists contributing to the IPBES assessment expressed hope governments will seek a careful balance between economic development and conservation.[52] The report called for "transformative changes" that will reduce agriculture's environmental footprint, slash wasteful consumption, and enforce restrictions on illegal fishing and logging.[52]

One example of what protected nature provides is a reliable source of fresh water. The value of that asset is high and growing higher. Another example is a carbon-sink sanctuary. A third example is a protected natural source of oxygen. A fourth example is a safe seafood supply. And the list of examples goes on and on...The total asset value is both priceless and astronomical!

Contrary to what is needed to preserve the biosphere (and its living residents), important laws like the Endangered Species Act have been under assault recently.[54] New policies give greater consideration to near-term economics than to species protection. Such policies are wrong-headed to ignore the long-term benefits of species diversity.

An excellent overview of how climate change is impacting the biosphere is a paper by Matthew Schwartz, a Harvard scholar.[55] He observes: "Global shifts in temperature, precipitation patterns, ocean levels, and the frequency of extreme weather events has impacted plant and animal populations as well as humans. The resulting extinctions, migrations, and behavioral changes will have catastrophic effects on entire ecosystems, fundamentally changing the world we inhabit. These transformations are already happening."[55] He notes the current annual loss of species is between 100 and 1000 per every 1 million species.

It should be noted that species extinction can be somewhat selective and can bear down on a whole class of species. One example is the host of reptiles that help keep balance in our habitat. Some 20% of all reptiles are facing near-term extinction.[74] New research published in Nature found that among those most threatened are turtles, snakes, lizards and crocodiles. Turtles are especially at risk: 60% of turtle species are most vulnerable.[74]

Culprits in the reptile slaughter include loss of habitat, hunting and fishing. Bruce Young, co-author of the study, says: "There's no rocket science in protecting reptiles, we have all the tools we need"---"Reduce tropical deforestation, control illegal trade and improve productivity in agriculture so we don't have to expand our agricultural areas". Dr. Young adds that these steps would also "help many, many, many other species".[74]

The researchers estimate that climate change affects extinction risks of 1 in 10 species.

Climate change impacts on the biosphere seem to be more focused on continents than on oceans. Increased attention on the oceans would be wise because inhabitants of continents would benefit greatly. Likewise, ignoring the oceans would be costly for continental inhabitants.

A new study titled "Avoiding Ocean Mass Extinction From Climate Change" was published in Science in April 2022.[75] Continuation of burning fossil fuels would cause ocean species extinction on a scale comparable to five mass extinctions in Earth's history. The worst catastrophe, 250 million years ago, was caused by global warming (started by volcanic eruptions). Between hotter oceans and reduced oxygen levels, 9 of 10 marine species perished.

The report also looked at benefits of holding carbon emissions within goals specified by the 2005 Paris accord. That would reduce marine extinction risks exceeding 70%. Princeton University geosciences professor Dr. Curtis Deutsch advised "Our choices have huge impacts".[75] United Nations Secretary General Antonio Gutrerres recently warned the ambitious goal of limiting warming to 1.5 degrees Celsius was "on life support".[75] The international community is still falling short in emission cut pledges needed for the Paris accord goals to materialize.

A recent commentary in Scientific American [88] mentioned that large ocean areas have lost 10%-40% of oxygen content and about 40% of the global population depends on ocean species to maintain livelihoods.

The possibility of a mass extinction that might include humans cannot be discounted. There have been five mass extinctions in Earth's history, each associated with a high concentration of carbon dioxide in the oceans.[56.] Adam Frank, a astrophysics professor at the University of Rochester, makes the point that "if we don't take the right action soon the biosphere will simply move on without us. So we must be honest. The problem is not saving the Earth or life writ large, but saving our civilization."[57]

Climate change is already killing people. Global warming, which makes heat waves more intense and more frequent, is killing people by exposing them to extreme heat.[58.] Heat deaths in Arizona and Nevada totaled 374 in 2017—more than triple the total in 2014. According to Dr. Rupa Basu, a California environmental health official, these numbers are conservative, because "[h]eat-related deaths are just very underreported."[58]

The U.S. federal government's Global Change Research Program forecasts "tens of thousands of additional premature deaths per year across the United States by the end of this century."[58] Record-breaking temperatures and high humidity made the southern U.S. states less habitable in summer 2020. Phoenix hit 114 degrees at Sky Harbor Airport and Houston had a heat index of 111 at Bush International Airport.[2.] The situation could be worse in other parts of the world, and places like North Africa and the Middle East risk becoming "unihabitable."[58.] In Summer 2020, floodwaters in China drowned 141 people, destroyed 28,000 homes, and displaced millions.[59] That same summer, the temperature in one city in Siberia reached 100°F, while a 6-month heat wave across the region was 9°F above average temperatures recorded between 1951 and 1980.[60] In other words, the habitat-friendly biosphere for humans has begun to shrink.

Global warming and climate change are creating negative consequences for Earth's plant and animal life. Global warming is also killing marine life, such as coral reefs. Biodiversity is shrinking from the rising temperatures.[61] Extreme marine heat waves, like the infamous "blob" off the U.S. West Coast, have caused massive die-offs, from invertebrates to mammals.[61] A study reported in Nature Climate Change surveyed 116 previously published papers, which yielded data from 1000 different ecological records. Together with other data sets, these records quantified biodiversity across different regions. This allowed risk assessment and detection of cascading effects between neighboring ecosystems. The researchers found the regions hardest hit by extreme temperatures were coral reefs in the Caribbean, sea grass in Australia, and kelp forests off the coast of California.[61] It should be noted that loss of marine plant life returns carbon to the environment when the ecosystem dies. Another study, published in the journal Science, discovered that climate change is reducing fish stocks. Combined with overfishing, the overall reduction can exceed 30%.[61]

Climate change threats to the biosphere are simply too vast to summarize in these pages. Narrowing the focus to one specific situation can help readers to appreciate the scale of climate change threats across Earth's biosphere. The situation chosen for emphasis is that of coral reefs.

The Plight of Coral Reefs

Heat waves in the oceans are raising temperatures above the threshold that corals can tolerate. These cause the tiny coral animal, called the polyp, to reject attached algae they need to survive. This damage to the coral is called bleaching, and it turns the normally brilliant colors to a ghostly white. Coral reefs are also attacked and weakened by higher acid levels in the ocean caused by elevated CO_2 absorption. Reduced carbonate ions make it more difficult for corals to develop their skeletons.[62] Both heat waves and higher acid levels are sickening and killing coral reefs. About one-half of global coral reefs are now dead.[63] Many places where coral reefs exist today will not be suitable habitats by 2045.[64.] Scientists forecast that 70%–90% of current coral reefs will be extinct in the next 20 years.[64] Over 130 million people depend on coral reefs for food and livelihood connected to fishing and tourism. [62] The loss of those reefs would likely be a humanitarian crisis in adjoining regions.[65]

Why should we care? The answer is coral reefs are critical for human survival, as well as that of many thousands of other species. They supply one-half of Earth's oxygen, absorb nearly one-third of all fossil fuel sourced CO_2, and are a necessary habitat for one-fourth of all fish species.[66] Coral reefs are fundamental components in nature's apparatus to make Earth habitable for plant and animal life—including humans.

A 2018 study found the number of days per year oceans experienced heat waves had increased 54% in the last 30 years.[61] Heat waves are deadly to coral reefs. A heat wave is defined as abnormally high temperatures persisting at least 5 consecutive days. One study found the median time between severe heat waves is now only 6 years.[67] This short time between damaging heat waves does not permit corals sufficient time to recuperate. Corals usually require 10–15 years to recover from severe heat waves.[67] Professor Sean Connolly at James Cook University in Queensland makes this general observation: "When climate change is too fast for adaptation to keep up, then lots of things go extinct."[68] Unfortunately, The Great Barrier Reef (running over 1,100 miles in the Pacific Ocean) was hit by another disastrous heat wave in summer 2020.[69]

A recent report updates the disastrous decline in coral reefs but also available opportunities to reverse that decline.[78] This report issued by the International Coral Reef Initiative blames climate change for much of the 14% decline between 2009 and 2019. Dr. David Obura, one of the report's editors, advises: "Coral reefs are the canary in the coal mine telling us how quickly it can go wrong".[78] One significant change during the 2009-2019 decade is how corals recover from heat waves. Early in the decade corals could recover quickly but lately the recovery is slow or not at all. Research scientist Serge Planes: "Since 2009, it's a constant decline at the global level". Over 300 scientists from 73 countries prepared the report.

On the positive side, the report said: "Many of the world's coral reefs remain resilient and can recover if conditions permit". Dr. Obura pleaded "We need to keep them functioning so that people's livelihoods can continue".[78] More recent reports echo this optimism but note that few new methods have matured to be ocean ready.[76,77] Efforts to save coral reefs need to be greatly expanded. That goal is made explicit in Chapter 11.

As global warming continues to heat the atmosphere and oceans, the incidence and severity of marine heat waves will continue to increase. There is no reliable remedy to the climate change assault on coral reefs (and other habitat components) other than to halt the warming trend. The increasing loss of coral reefs is tragic; however, there is one climate outcome that is more tragic: the permanent loss of environmental habitat that supports coral life. Near-extinction of coral habitat is predicted to occur by 2100.[64] With that outcome comes the loss of an important oxygen source, carbon sink, and habitat for numerous fish species. According to the Great Barrier Reef

Authority, "[c]limate change remains the single greatest challenge to the reef.[69]

Marine Carbon Reservoirs

As noted in Chapter 5, large carbon deposits in the oceans represent "grave risks for amplified climate disasters".[79] Unfortunately, available information on these deposits is sparse, such as how many are yet to be detected and their sizes.[80] Filling this information gap warrants priority action (as proposed in Chapter 11). But what are these deposits and why are they so dangerous? The following paragraphs summarize what is currently known.

Much of the marine carbon is currently locked up under frozen permafrost or ice-like carbon hydrates in or under the seabed. But global warming is heating the oceans (by absorbing 93% of the excess heat) and shallow ocean locations are already nearing thawing temperatures.[79 81] If much of the marine carbon (especially methane) were to escape into the atmosphere it could make Earth uninhabitable.[82] A major Tipping Point might be reached in the not-too-distant future.

Global methane levels in the atmosphere set a record one-year increase in 2021. This increase was greater than any in the last four decades (since measurements began).[83] Is this the beginning of the carbon emissions surge mentioned as a possibility in Chapter 2?

Methane is an immediate concern because its 100-year global warming potential is estimated to be 23 times greater than that of CO_2.[80] Methane is 84 times more potent greenhouse gas than carbon dioxide and it can linger in the atmosphere for at least a decade.[79]

Greenhouse gases in the marine environment are emitted by decaying organic material in the vicinity of geothermal vents deep under sea and also by decaying organic material within the seabed. Sometimes the geothermal gases feed into huge pools deep in the earth.[84 85 86] Other times they bubble up through numerous cracks in Earth's crust until blocked by frozen permafrost; become icy hydrates; are consumed by microbes; or escape into the atmosphere. This activity has been continuing for millions of years[87] but greenhouse gas leaks to the atmosphere might now be amplified by unprecedented post- Ice Age ocean warming (including likely permafrost thawing in the Arctic and Antarctic seabeds).

Greenhouse gas leaks from ocean sources have been recently documented in the Arctic,[81 85 87] Antarctic,[82] Pacific Northwest,[79] Mauritania,[84] British Colombia, [84] NE U.S. (Hudson Canyon)[84] and the Mariana Arc in the Pacific.[79]

This concludes Chapter 7.

Chapters 6 and 7 have summarized a broad spectrum of global warming and climate change threats. Taken together, these threats have immense significance. Yet, they may be only the beginning of a long tragic period for society if global warming is not fully arrested in the next one to two decades. This situation will not solve itself. As the U.N. report on biodiversity indicated, transformational changes are required. The choice for society seems rather simple: End carbon emissions in the short term to avoid future climate disasters of increasing severity OR continue avoiding actions needed to quickly reduce greenhouse gas emissions to zero. Whatever is decided, it will hopefully be the result of a conscious decision rather than inaction by default. The latter would be a sad commentary for a so-called civilized society.

Chapter 7 Sources

1. Dr. Aaron Berstein, "Coronavirus, Climate Change and the Environment," Harvard School of Public Health, August 7, 2020, pp. 1-8 (I2865)

2. John Schwartz, "Wilting Heat, Intensified by Climate Change," New York Times, July 16, 2020, p. A13 (I2855)

3. Lisa Friedman, "Study Finds a Link Between Air Pollution and Virus Deaths," New York Times, April 8, 2020, p. A16 (I2814)

4. University of New South Wales, "Leaving Microbes Out of Climate Change Conversation Has Major Consequences, Experts Warn," Science Daily, June 18, 2019, pp. 1-2 (I2687)

5. Maryn McKenna, "Deadly Kingdom," Scientific American, June 2021, pp. 26-35 (I3064)

6. Brenda Goodman, "Warmer Temps Speed Infections," WebMD, February 16, 2017, pp. 1-5 (I2688)

7. William Quarles, "Global Warming Means More Pathogens," IPM Practitioner, January 1, 2017, pp. 1-5 (I2689)

8. John McKenna, "The Deadly Disease Being Released as the Ice Thaws," World Economic Forum, May 11, 2017, pp. 1-4 (I2690)

9. Abraham Lustgarten, "How Climate Change is Contributing to Skyrocketing Rates of Infectious Disease," Pro Publica, May 7, 2020, pp. 1-11 (I2822)

10. Richard C. Paddock, Muktita Suhartono, "Fires in Indonesia Spur Fears as Amazon Burns," New York Times, September 18, 2019, p. A4 (I2653)

11. Kendra Pierre-Louis, "Complex Wildfires Grow in Ferocity as the Earth Heats," New York Times, August 29, 2019, pp. 1, 8 (I2640)

12. Julie Turkewitz, "'Second Lung' in Africa is on Fire, Too," New York Times, August 28, 2019, p. A7 (I2639)

13. Staff, "That Shrinking Feeling," The Economist, October 19, 2019 p. 47 (I2776)

14. Manuela Andreoni, Christine Hauser, "Over 74,000 Fires are Raging in the Amazon," New York Times, August 22, 2019, p. A10 (I2625)

15. Maria Arreillago et al., "Walls of Fire Devour Thousands of Miles of Brazil's Tropical Wetlands," New York Times, September 5, 2020, p. A7 (I2886)

16. Nova Xavantina, Santarem, "On the Brink," The Economist, August 3, 2019, pp. 14-16 (I2611)

17. Simon Romero, "Amazon Forests Vanishing Fast, Not Just In Brazil," New York Times, August 31, 2019, p. 1 (I2644)

18. Ernesto Londono et al., "Acting to Quell the Criticism, If Not the Fires," New York Times, August 24, 2019, pp.1, 8 (I2633)

19. Editors, "Death Watch," The Economist, August 3, 2019, p. 7 (I2612)

20. Max Fisher, "How The Amazon Could Self-Destruct," New York Times, August 30, 2019, p. A6 (I2641)

21. Roberto Mangabeira Unger, "A Way to Save the Amazon," New York Times, August 27, 2019, p. A23 (I2635)

22. Staff, "The Blame Game," The Economist, November 17, 2018, pp.79-80 (I2441)

23. Staff, "Of Chain Saws and Supply Chains," The Economist, June 13, 2020, pp. 23-25 (I2842)

24. Staff, "The Global Economic Outlook During the COVID-19 Pandemic: A Changed World," The World Bank, June 8, 2020, p.1 (I2841)

25. Manuela Andreoni, Ernesto Londono, "Despite World's Outrage, Farmers in Amazon Remain Defiant," New York Times, August 27, 2019, p. A4 (I2636)

26. Manuela Andreoni et al., "As Scorched Amazon Smolders, Brazil Fights Against Global Outrage," New York Times, August 23, 2019, p. A6 (I2627)

27. Staff, "A World Without Beaches," The Economist, August 17, 2019, pp. 11-12 (I2622)

28. Manuela Andreoni, "Brazil Rejects Millions in Aid for Amazon Pledged by Leaders at G7," New York Times, August 28, 2019, p. A7 (I2638)

29. Staff, "At Loggerheads Over the Amazon," The Economist, March 20, 2021, pp. 29-30 (I3032)

30. Editors, "To Stop Pandemics, Stop Deforestation," Scientific American, June, 2020, p. 8 (I2837)

31. Naomi Oreskes, Nicholas Stern, "Climate Changes' Unknown Costs," New York Times, October 25, 2019, p. A27 (I2779)

32. Carol Davenport, Jeanna Smialek, "Federal Report on Finances Warns of Climate Havoc," New York Times, September 10, 2020, pp. B1, B4 (I2887)

33. Somini Sengupta, "Global Risks of Climate and Debt," New York Times, April 8, 2021, pp.B1, B4 (I3044)

34. Alan Rappeport, Lisa Friedman, "Reluctant Nod From U.S. as Finance Ministers Issue Statement on Climate Threats," New York Times, February 24, 2020, p. A6 (I2801)

35. Paul Bodner, Tamara Grbusic, "Your Climate Disaster Tax Bill is Rising," New York Times, June 24, 2020, p.A23 (I2846)

36. Lisa Friedman, "Auditor Issues Warning on Climate Change Costs," New York Times, October 24, 2017, p. A17 (I2128)

37. Kendra Pierre-Louis, "These Billion-Dollar Natural Disasters Set a Record in 2017," New York Times, January 9, 2018, p. A9 (I2184)

38. D.R. Reidmiller et al., "Fourth National Climate Assessment, Vol. II, Overview" U.S. Government, Global Change Research Program, November 23, 2018, pp. 33-71 (I2691)

39. Coral Davenport, Kendra Pierre-Louis, "U.S. Climate Study Has Grim Warning of Economic Risks," New York Times, November 24, 2018, pp. 1, 17 (I2447)

40. Mitch Smith et al., "Floods Cost Farmers Livestock and Livelihoods," New York Times, March 19, 2019, pp.1,16 (I2511)

41. Christopher F. Schuetze, "As Drought Cripples the Rhine River, German Commerce Feels the Pain," New York Times, November 5, 2018, p. A10 (I2437)

42. Henry Fountain, "Climate Change Fuels Huge Drought in West, Increasing Risk of Fire," New York Times, May 20, 2021, p. A17 (I3063)

43. Staff, "Skiing Goes Downhill," The Economist, January 27, 2018, pp. 51-55 (I2189)

44. Somini Sengupta, "How Climate Change Disrupts Olive Industry," New York Times, October 25, 2017, p. A4 (I2131)

45. Bob Litterman, "The High Costs of Climate Risks," New York Times, January 30, 2019, p. A25 (I2485)

46. Staff, "After the Deluge," The Economist, February 23, 2019, pp. 62-63 (I2497)

47. Staff, "Blown Cover," The Economist, September 21, 2019, pp. 77-8 (I2656)

48. Staff, "Hot, Unbothered," The Economist, February 23, 2019, pp. 15-16 (I2496)

49. D.R. Reidmiller et al., "Forth National Climate Assessment, Vol. II, Summary Findings," U.S. Government, Global Change Research Program, November 23, 2018, pp. 1-9 (I2692)

50. Staff, " It's Not the Heat, It's the Cupidity," The Economist, July 15, 2017, p. 66 (I2092)

51. Donald Wuebbles et al., "U.S. Global Change Research Program, Climate Science Special Report (CSSR)," NOAA, June 28, 2017, pp. 1-669 (I2608)

52. Brad Plumer, "Report Details Global Shrink in Biodiversity," New York Times, May 7, 2019, pp.1,10 (I2538)

53. IPBES, "U.N. Report: Nature's Dangerous Decline 'Unprecedented'; Species Extinction Rate 'Accelerating,'" (press release), United Nations IPBES, May 6, 2019, pp. 1-18 (I2748)

54. Lisa Friedman, "U.S. Weakens Law Protecting Species at Risk," New York Times, August 13, 2019, pp. 1,11 (I2619)

55. Matthew Schwartz, " Ecosystem Shift: How Global Climate Change is Reshaping the Biosphere," Harvard University (SITN), June 30, 2014 (I2695)

56. Mark Fischetti, "Killer Seas," Scientific American, January 2018, p. 80 (I2181)

57. Adam Frank, "Earth Will Survive. We May Not," New York Times, June 13, 2018, p. A25 (I2230)

58. Christopher Flavelle, Nadja Popovich, "Heat-Related Deaths Rise in Southwest as Temperatures Spike," New York Times, August 27, 2019, p. A13 (I2637)

59. Staff, "A Deluge of Doubts," The Economist, July 18, 2020, p.34 (I2857)

60. John Schwartz, "Punishing Weather in Siberia That Didn't Have To Happen," New York Times, July 16, 2020, p. A12 (I2856)

61. Sarah Gibbens, "Ocean Heat Waves are Killing Underwater Life, Threatening Biodiversity," National Geographic, March 4, 2019, pp. 1, 2 (I2699)

62. Staff, "No Longer in the Pink," The Economist, October 26, 2019, p.12 (I2693)

63. Rebecca Albright, "Scientists Are Taking Extreme Steps to Help Corals Survive," Scientific American, January 2018, pp. 43-49 (I2180)

64. Renee Setter, "Warming, Acidic Oceans May Eliminate Coral Reef Habitats by 2100," American Geophysical Union, February 18, 2020, pp. 1-3 (I2747)

65. Damien Cave, "Rising Sea Temperatures Mar Great Barrier Reef," New York Times, April 7, 2020, p. A19 (I2813)

66. Jamail Dahr, "Coral Reefs, Life, Food, Oxygen at Risk," Global Catholic Climate Movement, May 25, 2017, pp. 1-16 (I2698)

67. Kendra Pierre-Louis, Brad Plumer, "Global Warming Takes Toll on Coral Reefs," New York Times, January 5, 2018, p. A9 (I2182)

68. Jacqueline Williams, "Deterioration of Great Barrier Reef Quickens," New York Times, July 5, 2018, p. A7 (I2259)

69. Richard Perez-Pena, "Climate Crisis Ravages Great Barrier Reef With 3rd Mass Bleaching Event in Five Years," New York Times, March 27, 2020, p. A18 (I2809)

70. Carl Zimmer, "Climate Change Will Quicken Viral Spillover, Study Finds", New York Times, May 3, 2022, p. D3 (I3163)

71. Chelsea Harvey, "Wildfires Could Transform Amazon from Carbon Sink to Source", Scientific American (E&E News), January 14, 2020, pp. 1-6 (3114)

72. Manuela Andreoni, "Deforestation of the Amazon Skyrocketed to a 15-Year High", New York Times, November 20, 2021, p. A4 (I3120)

73. Henry Fountain, "9.3 Million Acres of Old Tropical Forests Lost", New York Times, April 29, 2022, p. A8 (I3161)

74. Catrin Einhorn, "From Tiny Geckos to King Cobras, 20% of Reptiles Face Extinction Risk", New York Times, April 28, 2022, p. A9 (3160)

75. Catrin EinHorn, "Study Warns of a Mass Extinction at Sea if Emissions Aren't Cut", New York Times, April 30, 2022, p. A17 (I3162)

76. Staff, "Reef Knots", The Economist, June 4, 2022, pp. 70-71 (I3172)

77. Staff, "Surmounting Great Barriers" The Economist, June 4, 2022, pp. 12-13 (I3173)

78. Catrin Einhorn, "Coral Reefs in Decline Worldwide, Study Finds", New York Times, October 6, 2021, p. A11 (I3116)

79. Todd Woody, "Hugh Amounts of Greenhouse Gases Lurk in the Oceans, and Could Make Warming Far Worse", Nationalgeographic.com, December 17, 2019, pp. 1-3 (I2722)

80. Thomas Weber, et. al., "Global Ocean Methane Emissions Dominated by Shallow Coastal Waters", Nature Communications, October 8, 2019, pp. 1-6 (partial) (I3113)

81. Julia Steinbach, et. al. "Source Apportionment of Methane Escaping the Subsea Permafrost in the Outer Eurasian Arctic Shelf", doi.org PNAS, March 1, 2021, pp. 1-8 (partial) (I3107)

82. Bob Yirka, "Active Leak of Sea-Bed Methane Discovered in Antarctica for the First Time", PHYS.ORG, July 22, 2020, pp. 1-3 (I3112)

83. Raymond Zhong, "Methane Emissions, Noxious to Climate, Soared to Record in 2021, Scientists Say", New York Times, April 8, 2022, p. A17 (I3151)

84. Richard J. Davies, "Climate Driven Instability of Marine Methane Hydrate Along a Canyon-Incised Continental Margin", Geology, April 28, 2021, pp. 973-977 (I3109)

85. F.D. Szakal, "A Massive Methane Reservoir is Lurking Beneath the Sea", doi.org Eos, April 27, 2021, pp. 1-4 (I3110)

86. Bob Yirka, "Testing Waters of East Siberian Arctic Ocean Suggests Origin of Elevated Methane is Reservoir in Laptev Sea", PHYS.ORG, March 2, 2021, pp, 1-2 (I3111)

87. Andreia Plaza-Faverola, et.al., "Seabed Methane Release Follows Rhythm of the Tides" ScienceNorway.no, July 2, 2021, pp. 1-7 (I3108)

88. Nathalie Goodkin, Julie Pullen, "Let Oceans Breathe", Scientific American, April, 2022, p. 11 (I3148)

Chapter 8: Society's Response to Climate Threats

Introduction

Human responses to climate threats are manifested on several levels, and in this chapter those responses are categorized as follows:

International responses

Responses of the United States and other nations

State and local government responses

Private sector responses

How is sense made of society's response to a situation? That probably depends on the situation and specific factors related to it. The situation at hand is climate change and all-encompassing realities. The three chapters before this one describe unprecedented climate threats to the survival and wellbeing of life on Earth, including human life. Has this cumulative threat been communicated and discussed throughout society? Most likely not. So, it does not seem fair to judge society's response to a situation that is not fully understood.

Threat components like (1) approaching near-term tipping points, (2) carbon release threat from thawing permafrost and marine carbon reserves, and (3) limited global economic capacity to accommodate rising disaster costs all need to be reasonably understood (including risks embedded in uncertainties). Economic threats alone are considered by leading economists to be underestimated. A fair appreciation of climate crisis magnitude and urgency depends on gauging the actual cumulative climate threat.

Society has thus far responded to the climate threat it understood. Part of the problem is corrupted public information and lack of constructive debate (as discussed in Chapter 9). Another part of the problem is that international conferences attended by national leaders have been largely ineffective[1] in committing to necessary reductions in carbon emissions (see Chapter 9).

It seems a fundamental issue to gaining support for effective climate action is one of priority. The U.N. Secretary General worried out loud in April 2022 that nation's addiction to fossil fuels was outweighing urgency to combat climate change.[27] He said that addiction was "madness" and "We are sleepwalking to climate catastrophe".[27] John Kerry addressed a group of national ministers in January 2022 with the message "We all must move faster" to combat climate change.[28] That same week China stated it would not slash carbon emissions at the sacrifice of priorities such as food and energy for the masses.[28]

Rising energy prices are spurring greater production of fossil fuels that release greenhouse gases responsible for global warming.[29] U.S. climate initiatives are taking a backseat to energy price concerns.[30] President Biden's climate and energy goals could be largely pushed out of his first term agenda. It seems climate action priority is weakened by a lack of understanding the risks and severity of the cumulative climate threat. Better understanding of this threat should lead towards increased priority for urgent and crisis-level climate action.

Meanwhile, society at large has been working to slow global warming by reducing greenhouse gas emissions. These efforts are commendable, and cleaner production of electrical energy is making progress towards reducing emissions. Clean energy technology is gaining maturity, as reviewed in Chapter 11.

The principal assessment and principal conclusions for this book are provided and discussed in Chapter 10. These capture the essence of how society is doing in responding to the climate crisis. The answer is not very well, as measured against cumulative climate threat severity. A few remarks on society's response are made in the following paragraph, but the reader is referred to Chapter 10 for further explanation.

The current climate effort is deeply flawed and dangerously mismatched to the cumulative climate threat. Both that threat's magnitude and its urgency are seriously underestimated. It should be no surprise society's response to the climate threats falls far below that of a major crisis. For example, two response deficits in magnitude are funding and organizational manning. Two deficits in urgency are scheduling priority and weak, untimely goals. An overall flaw spanning all activities is lack of coordinated and detailed planning, based on specific project objectives. In other words, climate action is not dressed for combat with global warming. Chapter 11 outlines remedies to this situation.

International Responses

Climatologists and other specialists in numerous nations have been studying global warming phenomena for over three decades. In 1988, an international group, the Intergovernmental Panel on Climate Change (IPCC), was formed to monitor and summarize significant findings from that worldwide research.[2] The IPCC has published a series of reports, among which was the 2016 report quoted in Chapter 9 (Unnatural Causes of Global Warming). Early IPCC reports hedged on a human role in global warming, but by 2007, the IPCC reported 90% certainty of human causes. By 2013, the stated odds were at least 95%.[2] Later reports quoted still higher consensus.

The IPCC reports have been highly detailed in covering causes, observed impacts, predicted impacts, and means for combating climate change. Carbon dioxide levels have increased 41% since the Industrial Revolution, and could double in a few decades.[1] The March 2014 report synthesized 73,000 published works[3].

Another international response (independent of the IPCC activity) has been a long series of summit meetings between national leaders. The hope has been to strike an international agreement to curb carbon emissions. One summit, held in Kyoto, Japan, did manage a limited pact, but lacked strong commitments from all parties. Finally, in mid-December 2015, a climate deal was struck in a Paris summit meeting.[4] The Paris deal was agreed to by

195 nations, and a signing ceremony was held April 2, 2016 at U.N. headquarters in New York City.[5]

The Paris Agreement consists of voluntary emission control goals set by each nation. The collective goal is to stop global warming from exceeding 1.5°C rise above the mid-1860s level (with the realization that a 2.0°C rise is probably more practical). The expert estimate of likely rise (based on current goals in the Paris Agreement) is 2.7°C.[6] Nations were to do better when they met in Glasgow to reset goals.[1] The current level of global warming increase is already 1.2°C since the mid-1800s.

COP 26, as the Glasgow climate summit was known, fell painfully short of widespread increases in national emission-cut goals. In effect, that objective was kicked down to COP 27, scheduled to meet in November 2022 at the Egyptian resort of Sharm el-Sheikh.[31]

This "kick-down-the-road" situation is not unfamiliar with international climate summits (see Chapter 9 discussion of "institutional inertia"). It underscores the great difficulty in reaching global consensus on how to deal with climate change. Unfortunately, this kind of situation is often the case with Earth's international community, which is comprised of competing sovereigns. The goal of negotiating common cause can seem infinitely frustrating.

Still, COP 26 made some notable progress.[31] Assorted coalitions, known as "coalitions of the willing", managed to coalesce around limited, but important, climate goals. These included reducing methane emissions; eliminating coal burning power plants and reducing deforestation. However, none of the deals made were agreed unanimously.[32] One notable agreement was to slash their collective methane emissions 30% by 2030. This coalition deal was supported by 100 countries![32]

COP 26 did not quite give up on the Paris accord goal to hold global warming to 1.5 degrees centigrade increase over pre-industrial levels. But, the large gap between required emission cuts and cumulative nationally-pledged cuts is forcing growing recognition of that goal's futility.[31,32] The 1.5 degrees goal is considered necessary to avoid the worst consequences of global warming. Now, those consequences are looking more inevitable (based on current climate action plans).

COP 26 also revealed some uncertainty on whether national commitments to net-zero emissions by 2050 (or later) will actually be honored,[32] There is limited transparency and details on how nations expect to reach that goal (see Chapter 10 for discussion of other problems with the net-zero concept). There is also the question of whether a carbon emissions surge can be avoided (see Chapter 2).

Many specialists believe fossil fuel emissions must be ended by mid-century to avoid catastrophic climate consequences. However, national plans under the Paris accord do not go beyond 2030, and no nation has produced a workable strategy to end carbon emissions altogether.[5] Meanwhile, hundreds of new coal-burning power plants are planned to be built (mostly in developing countries).[5] Global demand for oil has not yet peaked, and is not expected to peak before sometime in the 2030s.[6] The lofty goals of the Paris Agreement are clearly out of step with realistic expectations, absent a fundamental rethinking of how to combat global warming.

The urgency of global action to slash greenhouse gas emissions is gaining important recognition and support. A new report from the Intergovernmental Panel on Climate Change (IPCC) calls for accelerated action.[33,34] To remain close to Paris Accord goals, the international community must reduce cumulative global emissions 43% by 2030. Current national plans add up to only a few percentage points by that time.[33] Also, to achieve the 1.5 degrees cap on global warming, the IPCC report claims "would require nations to all but eliminate their fossil fuel emissions by 2050"[34] This IPCC position acknowledges the need for a zero emissions goal by 2050 - significantly earlier than the net-zero emissions goal by 2050. By definition, the net-zero emissions goal allows polluting activities to continue until 2050 and probably beyond (see Chapter 10 discussion on problems with the net-zero emissions concept).

The IPCC's call for urgent climate action may not take into account three ticking time bombs: thawing permafrost emissions (Chapter 4); a potential carbon emissions surge (Chapter 2) and near-term emissions from marine carbon reservoirs (Chapter 7). These time-sensitive threats add to the necessity and prudence for immediate, scaled up climate action.

In addition to the difficulties outlined above, the Paris Agreement is far from being a robust international treaty. It is a consensus agreement, because it was felt that full treaty ratification by member states might be too much to expect. The downside of its being a consensus agreement is that it might be effectively ended by the withdrawal of one or more parties to the pact. It may be the best chance for an international commitment to climate security, but it is a fragile chance at best.

Responses of the United States and Other Nations

The contributions made by national programs to reduce carbon emissions are a vital component of international efforts. China, for example, is making exemplary strides, as are numerous other nations.

President Barack Obama exercised leadership in championing global and national efforts to mitigate global warming. He took personal responsibility to help assure the Paris Agreement was concluded on best-possible terms. He also nurtured environmental policies through the Environmental Protection Agency (EPA).

U.S. climate policies have now taken a sharp turn towards combating climate threats with the 2020 presidential election of Joseph R. Biden Jr.[10] Ernest Moniz, advisor to the campaign, remarked: "We have to re-establish American leadership globally on climate change."[7] In President Biden's inaugural address on January 20, 2021, he mentioned "a time of testing" and "a climate in crisis."[8] Going into this address, he was already organizing the White House to emphasize climate policy throughout the administration.[9] He established a new climate "nerve center" within the White House under Gina McCarthy, former head of the Environmental Protection Agency (in the Obama Administration).[9]

One of President Biden's first executive orders was to start the 30-day process of rejoining the Paris climate accord.[10] Mr. Biden remarked, "We're going to combat climate change in a way we have not before." His ambitious climate agenda includes replacing Mr. Trump's rollbacks with new regulations. He will likely face opposition from Republicans and some business groups.[10] Republican Senators Mitch McConnell (Kentucky) and John Barrasso (Wyoming) represent coal states and would be expected to be among critics of such new legislation.[11]

President Biden is a strong advocate clean energy and other climate security objectives but lately has encountered strong headwinds that challenge his climate agenda. Those headwinds include U.S. Supreme Court skepticism over EPA authority regulate emissions[35] and fast-rising energy costs, related to inflation and the war in Ukraine.[30] These happen to be situations over which he has limited leverage.

Mr. Biden is now reshaping climate and energy policy to an extent some might see as an overreaction to the challenging headwinds. For example, he is opening 145,000 acres of public land for oil drilling.[36] He has also temporarily removed summer bans on the use of an ethanol-gasoline blend reputed to worsen summer smog.[37]

Climate change seems to be losing priority to near-term pressing issues. As mentioned in the previous section, China is also giving domestic needs priority over climate commitments. India has also shown a tendency to favor industrial development over climate initiatives. The U.S., China and India are responsible for a major share of cumulative global pollution. Their leadership towards global climate security is urgently needed at this pivotal moment in history. (Global climate security is defined near the end of Chapter 10).

State and Local Governments

Across the globe, government jurisdictions below the national level are demonstrating progress towards carbon-fee economies. As an example, state and local governments in the U.S. are de facto implementing President

Obama's Clean Power Plan.[12] Thirty-three states and the District of Columbia have cut emissions while growing their economies in the period between 2000 and 2014.[12] New York and California plan to cut emissions 40% below 1990 levels by 2030. Massachusetts issued new rules for power plants and vehicles to cut 1990 level emissions 25% by 2020. Emissions there are already down 20%.[12]

Cities across the globe are also taking aggressive steps to cut carbon emissions. Over 10,000 climate initiatives are being implemented in cities worldwide.[13] The Compact of Mayors, representing 228 cities (438 million citizens), has pledged to avoid 2 billion metric tons of greenhouse pollution per year.[14] One analysis estimates the total cut by all cities could reach 8 billion metric tons by 2050. Some cities, like Copenhagen and Melbourne, have adopted plans to become carbon-neutral.[14]

In a recent speech, Michael Bloomberg, former NYC mayor, observed: "Cities, businesses, and citizens will continue reducing emissions because they have concluded...that doing so is in their own self-interest."[13] The Republican mayor of San Diego, Kevin Faulconer, is among the government officials taking leadership responsibility for accelerating solutions to global warming. His climate action plan commits San Diego to be on 100% renewable energy by 2035. Other cities are taking notice of his example.[13] Cities produce up to 70% of all greenhouse emissions worldwide.

Private-Sector Responses

There is a broad array of public responses. Beginning with non-governmental organizations (NGOs), many citizens are engaged by supporting climate-action groups. These groups represent millions of citizens when they act to change public policies and priorities to combat global warming. From the Sierra Club to Greenpeace to the Union of Concerned Scientists to the Environmental Defense Fund, etc., they each have a role in the collective goal of a world free from the threat of climate catastrophes. Aside from their individual action agendas, the climate action groups are networked to work together. The Climate Action Network (CAN) international has 1,100 NGO members in over 120 countries.

USCAN has 160 member groups. These networks and member groups have web pages on the Internet that provide specific information about their activities.

Action by special-interest groups is another form of public expression. In mid-2016, shareholders pressed oil companies to institute more responsible climate policies.[15] A third kind of public expression is marching on the streets to demonstrate the need for climate action. One hundred thousand demonstrators marched on New York City streets to warn of climate disaster in September 2014.[16] A fourth kind of public political action is through specific initiatives like the Green New Deal and citizen groups like the Sunrise Movement.[17]

Then, there is the "one leader, many followers" movement in the name of Greta Thunberg (from Sweden). She has sparred with world leaders, including Mr. Trump. At Davos in January 2020, she and Mr. Trump exchanged words. Among his remarks, he stated "This is not a time for pessimism." She replied in her remarks: "Don't be so pessimistic."[18.] Ms. Thunberg regularly challenges world leaders at international conference venues to do more to slash carbon emissions. She has millions of followers, and she has traveled the world to observe the effects of climate change. More mature than her years, she is still a teenager at the time of this writing. She has raised the bar for future activists to follow.

Other evidence of public response is via opinion polls. One poll reported 64% of Americans are worried "a great deal" or "a fair amount" about global warming. The same poll found 71% do not favor U.S. withdrawal from the Paris accord.[19] A Pew poll in late 2015 determined there is global consensus on the need to curb emissions, but there are varying degrees of concern.[20] A January 2015 poll of 1,006 adults across the U.S. showed that 83% of Americans (including 61% of Republicans) believe there will be "very serious" or "somewhat serious" problems if nothing is done to reduce emissions.[24] The number of Americans who believe climate change is caused at least in part by human activity has grown from 72% in a 2011 poll to 81% in a 2015 poll.[21]

Also in the public domain are significant strides in developing new clean power technologies. The costs of clean power are dropping rapidly. Among clever innovations are ways of storing solar and wind power for later use. One way is to pump fluids or air into underwater tanks, then exploit underwater pressure to bring the air or fluids back to the surface to drive electricity-producing turbines.[22] Another way is to store electrical energy in banks of lithium-ion cells making up a huge battery.[23]

In late January 2021, General Motors announced it is ending production of fossil-fueled cars and trucks by 2035.[24] The all-electric decision is a strong move to reduce greenhouse gas emissions, and it demonstrates how industry initiative can be powerful in combating global warming.

Tesla has entered the clean energy arena by placing battery installations in power grids to draw charging power when rates are low and then supplying power during peak demand when rates are highest.[25] On the nuclear reactor power front, new technology is replacing old technology and smaller reactors are being developed for new markets.[26] A final example is new technology for carbon capture before emissions leave the smokestack. This small sample of new clean power technologies gives credence to optimism that global warming can be defeated in the long run. Chapter 11 expands on technological advances and reasons for optimism.

Chapter 8 Sources

1. Somini Sengupta, "New Targets for Emissions Fall Far Short of Paris Goals," New York Times, February 27, 2021, p. A9 (I3022)

2. Justin Gillis, "Climate Panel Near Certainty on Global Warming," New York Times, August 20, 2013, pp. A1, A7 (I1378)

3. Staff, "Climate Change: In the Balance," The Economist, April 5, 2014, pp. 70-71 (1416)

4. Editors, "The Paris Climate Talks," New York Times, December 15, 2015, p. A30 (I1651)

5. Justin Gillis, Carol Davenport, "Leaders Meet to Sign Climate Pact," New York Times, April 22, 2016, p. A12 (I1738)

6. Keith Bradsher, "Paris Deal on Climate Change is Official. Time to Fill in the Blanks," New York Times, November 4, 2016, p. B3 (I1870)

7. Carol Davenport, Lisa Friedman, "Biden Takes a 'Whole-Government Approach' to Fight Climate Change," New York Times, November 18, 2020, p. A19 (I2930)

8. Glen Thrush, "President Biden's Inaugural Address, Annotated," New York Times, January 21, 2021, p. A15 (I2978)

9. Lisa Friedman, "Climate 'Nerve Center' in Biden White House," New York Times, January 20, 2021, p. A16 (I2975)

10. Coral Davenport, Lisa Friedman, "Rejoining Paris Accord Tops Moves on Climate," New York Times, January 21, 2021, p. A21 (I2979)

11. Coral Davenport, Lisa Friedman, "Battle Lines Form Over Biden's Push on Climate," New York Times, January 27, 2021, pp. 1, 17 (I2985)

12. Editors, "On Climate Change, Look to the States," New York Times, December 26, 2016, p. A20 (I1944)

13. Jeff Biggers, "Cities Must Lead on Climate," New York Times, November 30, 2016, p. A23 (I1908)

14. David Biello, "Cities to the Rescue," Scientific American, December, 2014, pp 15, 19 (I1500)

15. Staff, "Greens in Pinstriped Suits," The Economist, May 21, 2016, p. 57 (I1750)

16. Staff, "As Governments Lag, Some Companies Step Up," New York Times, Sept. 24, 2014, pp. B1, B4 (I1475)

17. Michelle Goldberg, "The Green New Deal Made Markey Cool," New York Times, September 5, 2020, p. A23 (I2884)

18. Mark Landler, Somini Sengupta, "At Davos, Climate Showdown between the President and the Teenager," New York Times, January 22, 2020, p. A9 (I2735)

19. Staff, "The Burning Question," The Economist, November 26, 2016 p. 11 (I1896)

20. Sewell Chan, "Poll Finds Global Consensus on the Need to Curb Emissions," New York Times, Nov. 6, 2015, p. A9 (I1622)

21. Coral Davenport, Marjorie Connelly, "Most in GOP Say They Back Climate Action," New York Times, January 31, 2015, pp. A1, A11 (I1522)

22. Staff, "Depths of Imagination," The Economist, November 5, 2016, p. 70 (I1871)

23. Stanley Reed, "Harnessing Solar Power in the Dark," New York Times, November 28, 2016, p. B1, B7 (I1902)

24. Neal E. Boudette, Carol Davenport, "GM to Abandon Cars and Trucks Using Gas by 2035," New York Times, January 29, 2021, pp 1, 18 (I2990)

25. Diane Cardwell, "Moving Beyond Cars, Tesla Uses Batteries to Boost Power to Grid," New York Times, January 31, 2017, pp. B1, B7 (I1967)

26. Staff, "Nuclear Options," The Economist, January 28, 2017, p. 57 (I1965)

27. Lisa Friedman, "Warning of a 'Catastrophe' With the Use of Fossil Fuels" New York Times, March 22, 2022, p. A6 (I3146)

28. Lisa Friedman, "Kelly Tells Top Polluters "We All Must Move Faster to Fight Climate Change"', New York Times, January 28, 2022, p. A18 (I3129)

29. Patrick Cohen, "Fuel Costs Top Climate as Worry", New York Times, February 24, 2022, pp. B1,4 (I3138)

30. Tony Romm, Anna Phillips, "Biden Climate Initiatives Hit Snag With Energy-Price Upheaval", Seattle Times, Washington Post, March 19, 2022, p. A3 (I3145)

31. Staff, "Out of Reach? (After COP 26)", The Economist, November 20, 2021, pp. 57-8 (I3119)

32. Staff, "Are the Climate Goals Dead or Alive?", The Economist, November 13, 2021, pp. 80-81 (I3117)

33. Brad Plummer, Raymond Zhong, "Fossil Fuels Must Be Cut Faster, Panel Warns", New York Times , April 5, 2022, pp 1-6 (I3149)

34. Brad Plumer, et.al., "Time is Running Out to Fix Climate, Report Says", New York Times, March 1, 2022, pp. 1,8 (I3139)

35. Adam Liptak, Justices Dispute EPA Power to Cut Emissions", New York Times , March 1, 2022, pp. 1,16 (I3140)

36. Coral Davenport, "Biden to Open 145,000 Acres to Drillers, and Charge Them Higher Fees", New York Times , April 16, 2022, p. A22 (I3157)

37. Michael D. Shear, Lisa Friedman, "After Vow to Fix Climate, Biden Opens Fossil Fuel Spigot", New York Times , April 13, 2022, p. A16 (I3155)

Chapter 9: Obstacles to Climate Consensus

Introduction to Chapter 9

As explained in Chapter 10, efforts to combat global warming are falling short. Evidence of carbon emission reductions sufficient to reverse or halt the warming trend does not exist. Pledges for capping carbon emissions have become empty promises as national goals have been missed time and again. Also, there is no proof of a cost-effective, full scale, geoengineering plan for mitigating the climate crisis or safe consequences of its implementation. Nor is there a commitment of the resources necessary to implement such a plan. Global institutions such as the United Nations and summit conferences of national leaders are losing ground against the cascading climate disasters.

It's not that global warming has suddenly attacked the planet without warning. Calls for urgent climate action date to the 1980's.

It's not that global leaders have failed to work diligently to combat global warming. Many, if not most, have striven to find workable solutions to the growing threats.

It's not that the climate threat is impossible to defeat. There are available technologies, emerging technologies, and potential social adjustments that hold promise for reversing the warming trend (as explained in Chapter 11).

Without doubt, there are obstacles to achieving consensus on how to manage the climate change situation (as identified in this chapter). But the mere existence of obstacles is not proof these obstacles are insurmountable.

This first section of Chapter 9 examines how institutional inertia is a hurdle to combating global warming. "Institutions" mean organizations or other social structures leading global efforts to address the climate threat. "Inertia" refers to that aspect of organizations which resists movement towards specified goals. "Aspect" might be difficult to define as an abstraction, but it is not difficult to understand by observing how organizations behave.

Section One: Institutional Inertia

Concerns about air pollution and its effects date at least to the mid-20th century. However, a strong institutional response to environmental concerns probably did not materialize much before the public outcry on Earth Day (April 24, 1970). Global warming concerns were not widely recognized at that time, but computer model projections were soon to begin showing significant warming from greenhouse gas pollution.[1.] Perhaps the first major global institutional response was an international collaborative scientific study reported in January 1986.[1.] Coordinated by NASA and involving 150 scientists from 11 countries, this study confirmed that emissions from burning fossil fuels were changing atmospheric chemistry. Among the findings were that this pollution was worldwide and causing "appreciable greenhouse warming." Warming in the next 50 years was expected to be at a "rate twice that of the previous 130 years."[1]

This study was sponsored by a number of national and international organizations, including the NOAA (National Oceanic and Atmospheric Administration), the World Meteorological Organization, and United Nations Environmental Program. Measurement data utilized in the study included sensor measurements from NASA's Nimbus satellite.

The above study is an excellent example of global scientific collaboration, which has evolved as a respected institution of global society. This collaboration is happening every day as scientists exchange information and jointly prepare journal articles reporting their coordinated research.

The January 1986 study was no doubt helpful in calling public attention to the global warming situation. In June 1988, scientists and politicians gathered in Toronto for a "World Conference on the Changing Atmosphere." This conference called for a 20% reduction in CO_2 emissions by 2005.[2] By late 1988, U.S. News and World Report had published a relevant article[3], the U.S. Environmental Protection Agency (EPA) was drafting a climate report predicting dire consequences[4], and a U.S. Energy Department report warned of rising greenhouse gas emissions.[4] As public agitation continued to build in 1989, President Bush announced interest in global talks and an international convention on global warming.[5] When this announcement was made, U.S. delegates were already attending a global warming meeting in Geneva.

The second global institution (with key roles in combating global warming) recognized in this chapter is international conferences of sovereign nations (ICSN), loosely called "climate summit conferences." These conferences often result in an agreed pact or treaty, usually referred to the next scheduled conference for further action. ICSN is a convenient term used in this book, and is of prime interest in this chapter because of the institution's struggle to overcome inertia on climate issues. As will be seen, national sovereign interests can collide with global interests.

Before proceeding, it should be noted that by 2005, CO_2 emissions were not 20% lower (as called for by the 1988 Toronto conference), but rather 34% higher. They had increased an additional 22% by 2017.[2] CO_2 emissions are still rising, with no assured end in sight.

The international conference on global warming President Bush had called for finally occurred in June 1992, when a 12-day United Nations-hosted meeting convened in Rio de Janeiro. This ICSN was dubbed "The Earth Summit," and it produced an array of documents, including a Framework Convention on Climate Change. The Rio summit (as it was also known) was the first major ICSN to address global warming and climate change. It was to be followed by a long series of such ICSN meetings that continue to the present day. One such conference was on the fifth anniversary of the Rio summit.

A third group of global institutions with a critical role in combating climate change is made up of international organizations such as the United Nations (U.N.). The U.N. itself is a powerful advocate for environmental security. However, its powers are quite limited. It has no authority to take action except as granted by the sovereign nations (which have delegates as voting members of the U.N. General Assembly). The U.N. has no taxing authority and is dependent on dues paid by the sovereign members. It has limited assets with which to support day-to-day operations. Other international organizations have similar limitations, and many depend largely on charitable donations. To put this into perspective, no international entity has both the authority and resources to implement a global comprehensive plan for combating global warming. The planet is at the mercy of some 200 sovereign nations, many of which behave as though national interests take priority at all times. The discussion of sovereignty continues in Chapter 12.

ICSN climate summits (including interim preparation meetings) are a stage for viewing the realities of such endeavors. Ten weeks before the Rio summit, preparatory talks in New York City on two tentative accords for Rio had stalled.[6.] One concerned carbon dioxide reduction goals and the other was for providing pollution control technology to developing nations. A representative from the European Union complained U.S. intransigence could reduce Rio to an exercise in rhetoric. (This argument on carbon dioxide goals continued in Rio).[7]

A significant report on the status of goals set by the Rio climate summit came from a U.N. panel meeting 2 years later.[8] The 53-nation Commission on Sustainable Development concluded there were significant shortfalls. Chairman of the meeting, Klaus Topfer, remarked that Rio goals on financing environmental programs fell "significantly short of expectations and requirements." Also, efforts to formulate a global plan to save the world's shrinking forests were blocked by Brazil, which cited interference with its management of the Amazon forest. Other concerns included the need for "northern industrialized countries " to reduce energy consumption and garbage creation."[8] Note the clashes between national sovereign interests and global interests.

The next major assessment of Rio goals was at U.N. headquarters in NYC during a special session in June 1997. It was dubbed "Earth Summit +

5"[9], and brought together some 70 world leaders who worked in committees to gauge progress since Rio and to negotiate proposals in preparation for the next ICSNs (scheduled for Bonn and Kyoto in November and December 1997, respectively).The lack of environmental progress since Rio cast a sense of gloom over the meeting.[9] Few industrialized countries (including the U.S.) were expected to achieve the Rio goal of capping greenhouse gas emissions at 1990 levels by 2000.[10] Nearly all the Rio goals suffered setbacks. Bickering at Earth Summit + 5 did not help matters: there were no agreements on (1) cutting carbon emissions, (2) slowing deforestation, or (3) increasing aid to developing countries to assist environmental programs.[9] Or perhaps these chronic issues simply could not overcome inertia??

The Bonn ICSN did not fare much better. Two big stumbling blocks were disparity between emission control proposals and disputes on aid to developing countries.[11] The U.S. declared it would not sign a Kyoto accord unless developing nations pledged "meaningful" participation in emission cuts. The position of developing countries was that industrialized nations "became rich" through a century of uncontrolled emissions and should bear most of the cost of preventing future climate change. (This dispute continues to the present.) The Bonn ICSN ended in a pessimistic mood.[11] Perhaps there were also many headaches caused by institutional inertia??

The much-anticipated Kyoto ICSN convened in December 1997. Agreement on a treaty, which legally requires industrialized nations to slash greenhouse gas emissions, was reached on December 11. This Kyoto treaty was considered a major achievement by negotiators and a significant milestone in the ICSN climate series. ICSN meetings continued into the first decades of the third millennium.

In March 2014, a U.N. panel warned climate change effects could escalate substantially if global warming emissions are not controlled.[12] That panel was the Intergovernmental Panel on Climate Change (IPCC). This IPCC report noted that "two decades of international efforts to limit emissions have yielded little result."[12] This report was released as preparations were being made for yet another ICSN climate summit—this time in Lima, Peru.

Representatives from nearly 200 sovereign nations gathered in Peru in early December 2014 to begin two weeks of climate negotiations.[13] The "Lima Accord," as it would become known, provided preliminary language to be finalized in Paris talks the next year.[14].

Preparatory meetings for the Paris conference were hampered by bickering over the chronic issue of how much the rich nations should help the poor nations with climate change costs.[15] An earlier deal championed by Hillary Clinton had yielded a pledge from advanced industrialized nations to provide $100 billion per year by 2020. Nations were nowhere near that pledge level as the Paris talks approached.[16] Christina Figueres, an executive secretary at the United Nations, advised: "There is no credible roadmap to the $100 billion."[16]. Part of the financial aid problem seemed to be lack of an agreed definition of climate finance. Climate financing and development financing also seemed to be intertwined.

The above paragraph is filled with symptoms of institutional inertia.

Achievement of the Paris Treaty was highly celebrated by conference delegates, but there was recognition of shortfalls that required member nations to strengthen their commitments. For example, pledged emission controls were insufficient to meet the Conference goal of limiting the rise of global temperatures to 2°C. The pledge shortfall was 50%.[6] Total pledges would reduce greenhouse emissions through 2030, only 3% below the "business as usual" average rise of 8%.[17]

How does this compare to what is needed to stabilize emissions at a safe level? According to an IPCC scenario, global annual per capita emissions would need to be slashed from the current 5 metric tons to less than 1 ton by 2075.[17] In other words, the Paris emission controls are a pittance compared to what will be needed. Also, scientists advise that deep emissions cuts in the near future are far more effective than those in the distant future.[17].

The U.S. Supreme Court decided to halt implementation of President Obama's climate change legislation less than two months after Paris talks adjourned.[18.] This new regulation was key to honoring the U.S. pledge to slash carbon emissions. World reaction to the court's ruling made it clear this setback would likely make it more difficult for other nations to honor their pledges under the Paris Treaty.[18.] Although the court's ruling would likely face legal challenges, it added new uncertainty to a climate treaty already plagued by uncertainties.

Fourteen months later, world leaders gathered at U.N. headquarters for a Paris Treaty signing ceremony. The acknowledged reality was that signing the pact was not the end of work to control global warming, but the beginning. Among uncertainties clouding the pact's future were whether nations would strengthen their emission control pledges to assure global temperature increases remained below 2°C.[19]

On this last point, negotiations continued in Morocco in mid-November 2016. This meeting happened to occur about the same time as another relevant event: A report released by the International Energy Agency (IEA) warned the Paris deal was too weak to achieve its goal of holding global temperatures below a 2°C increase.[20.]

Moving ahead 13 months to mid-December 2017 in Boulogne, France, the ICSN climate story resumed during the proceedings of yet another climate summit. France's President Emmanuel Bacon was addressing the conference and was about to sum up the current status of climate negotiations when he declared: "We are losing the battle."[21]

On December 1, 2018, The Economist published an insightful article on efforts to combat global warming.[22.] After an overview of the climate threat and societal responses, it asked: "So why is the response inadequate?" One answer given was the clash of special interests that lobby hard to make consensus difficult. Then, the following statement was made: "But the chief reason is that the world has no history of dealing with such a difficult problem, nor the institutions to do so." So, while this section examines institutional inertia, the possibility that no existing institution is equal to the task should also be considered.

Within a few days after The Economist article was published, delegates to the 24th annual ICSN climate summit began arriving in Katowice, Poland. U.N. Secretary General Antonio Gutterres noted that "we are still not doing enough, to prevent irreversible and catastrophic climate destruction."[23] However the worsening situation since the Paris conference was dampening optimism. Many countries were not anywhere near meeting pledged emission controls; Russia had not ratified the Paris Treaty, and the United States had pulled out of it.[23.] Poland and others argued that if big polluters like the United States did not intend to honor their pledges, they should not expect countries to increase pledged emission cuts. Even so, U.S. officials attending the conference argued a rapid retreat from fossil fuels was unrealistic.[24] Trump's climate advisor, Wells Griffith, told a conference panel, "We strongly believe that no country should have to sacrifice their economic security or energy security in pursuit of environmental sustainability."[24] Protesters interrupted by chanting "Shame on you!"

There is additional evidence of Paris Accord signatories' continued failure to make adequate emission reduction pledges.[25] A roundup of national pledges in late February 2021 was still another disappointment. Patricia Espinosa, head of the U.N. climate agency, remarked that "current levels of climate ambition are very far from putting us on a pathway that will meet our Paris Agreement goals."[25.] A summary of follow-on Paris Accord activity in 2021 and 2022 is provided in Chapter 8 in the International Responses section.

In the 27-year period between Rio and Katowice, the sovereign powers have frequently pledged to cap carbon emissions. Those unenforceable, voluntary pledges have not yielded a permanent reduction in global emissions. Pollution emissions are still rising and are predicted to continue rising. If small emission reductions had begun 27 years ago, the planet would not now be forced to make large, immediate cuts to avoid cascading climate disasters that stress global financial resources and threaten Earth's habitat. The international climate conferences have failed to provide global climate security. The sovereign powers have not earned reliable trust to effectively manage the global climate change situation. Unfortunately, climate action options are now much more limited.

Section Two: Corrupted Information

Lies, Lies, and More Lies

Navigating the global information domain to make sense of a situation, one will encounter a minefield of corrupted information, including outright lies. Close cousins to lies are fabrication, falsification, fraud, forgery, and faked information. These all intend to misinform, and as one neuroscientist points out, "By lying we deny our friends access to reality—and their resulting ignorance often harms them in ways we did not anticipate."[26] He is speaking about lying between friends, but the scale of harm spreads far and wide when lies are told on the public stage.

Examples of public lies are listed below to illustrate their pervasiveness in society. Even this small sample indicates wide diversity in public lying:

1. Fake and substandard medicines are threatening both poor and advanced nations. One study reported in the American Journal of Tropical Medicine and Hygiene estimated 120,000 children in sub-Saharan countries under age 5 died because of ineffective malaria medicine.[27] Substandard antibiotics are also a problem. One study found 60% of tablets did not have sufficient active ingredients and a second study found 65% of samples were substandard. Many of the phony and substandard drugs originate in China and India.[27]

2. A Manhattan building inspector falsely certified that over 200 buildings were free of asbestos and lead. In truth, he did not conduct any of the required tests and the reports he filed were all lies. A number of the "inspected" buildings were subsequently demolished, which exposing demolition workers to dangerous substances. The city opened a special web page to register victims with the prosecutor's office.[28]

3. The largest-circulation newspaper in the U.S., USA Today, revealed that one of its top writers had fabricated portions of at least 8 major articles in the last 10 years. Jack Kelly, referred to as a "star foreign correspondent," also used the work of other news organizations without attribution. He also invented first-hand accounts (such as an encounter with a suicide bomber) to falsify his reports.[29.]

4. Fake passports allowed 30 "fugitives" to enter the U.S. without triggering any warnings, in a test conducted by the General Accountability Office (GAO). Sen. Susan Collins (R. Maine) commented, "These are exactly the kinds of problems that allowed the terrorists to attack our country…" Michael Johnson, a former State Department security official, faulted a lack of aggressive pursuit to catch black-market sellers of fake identification documents used to obtain fake passports. [30.]

5. It's an old debating trick to discredit one's opponent with a lie. During U.S. Senate testimony, Dr. Patrick Michaels of the University of Virginia employed this trick to discredit Dr. James Hansen, a NASA climatologist. This is how it worked. Dr. Michaels falsified a chart originated by Dr. Hansen by deleting two of three lines predicting global warming trends. Dr. Hansen's top line represented "higher than expected," the middle line "expected," and the bottom line "lower than expected." After deleting the two lowest lines, Dr. Michaels accused Dr. Hansen of exaggerating the warming threat. In truth, Dr. Hansen's middle line agreed closely with actual data. Dr. Michaels did not want the truth known. He repeated the lie in a number of public presentations.[31]

6. Bogus college degrees were offered for sale from a large scam based in Pakistan. Actors posed as professors. News reports were fabricated. College campuses existed only on computer servers. Sometimes fake degrees were sought out by willing buyers. Other times, buyers thought they were enrolling in a real college program.[32]The problem of faked degrees and college scams occurs in other fraudulent operations.

7. Forged documents and other lies were behind real estate swindles that landed Adam C. Hochfelder in prison. He pleaded guilty to 18 counts of

grand larceny and fraud. Victims of $17 million in losses included friends, family, and banks.[33]

8. Exxon spent $30 million to deceive the public into thinking climate change was uncertain even though the company was fully aware of climate threats to public welfare.[34]

9. Federal oil drilling regulators are faulted in an Inspector General's investigation for falsified reports and other ethical lapses. The Minerals Management Service has a reputation for lax oversight and questionable ties to the oil industry. It is believed federal inspectors receive favors from the industry they oversee.[35]

10. Four cancer charities were accused of fraud and lying in a May 2015 complaint filed by the Federal Trade Commission (FTC). The charities claimed to spend 100% of donations totaling $200 million on medical support services. "These were lies," noted the formal complaint. Actually, less than 3% was spent on cancer patients. Government officials stated this was the largest charity fraud on record.[36] The FTC calls these groups "sham charities."

11. How do you get 5-star Internet product reviews? By paying $2 per star, via a refund paid for the review. Such is an expedient way to buy fake reviews. Bogus endorsements are often difficult to distinguish from honest reviews, but are drawing attention of the Federal Trade Commission concerned with advertising practices.[37]

12. "Presidents lie for all kinds of reasons," according to Sean Wilentz, professor of history at Princeton University. "Richard Nixon lied because he was trying to save his presidency...Roosevelt misled the country over things like Lend-Lease in order to advance a policy he thought would save the world…Churchill advised Joseph Stalin, 'In wartime, truth is so precious that she should always be attended by a bodyguard of lies.'" A Gallup poll in April 2005 found most Americans thought President Bush "deliberately misled the American public" regarding Iraq's possession of weapons of mass destruction.[38]

13. The U.S. Department of Interior in the Trump administration deliberately inserted misleading climate statements into its policy documents.[39]

This litany of lies is closed with the following thought: Lies are lies, whether or not they are believed to be justified by the liar.

Not only lies

Corrupted information does not end with lies. Any information that is intentionally dishonest, less than 100% true, or factually incomplete is corrupted in one way or another. Listed below are various kinds of false or dishonest information:

Myths	Propaganda
Exaggeration	Deceit
Deception	Misleading information
Disinformation	Censored information
Distortion	Defective data/statistics
Spin	Factual errors

There are numerous, real-life examples of each kind listed above. In addition to corrupted information, the global information domain is polluted by other kinds of low-quality information: uninformed opinions, misinformed opinions, unfounded assertions, extremely biased opinions, sheer nonsense, etc. These useless types can be views as the debris field of information space. Finding uncorrupted information to make sense of a situation is a challenge to not be taken lightly. Rigorous research and attention to credible information sources can make the task manageable.

Section Three: Human Fallibility

Are humans perfect? This question is easily answered: people do not function perfectly. Even bodily processes like cell division and protein folding are imperfect. When a cell divides into two cells, they are normally identical, but occasionally, a malfunction produces one defective cell. Protein folding can also misfire, and a misfolded protein is the result (a protein is a chain of molecules that must fold into a precise shape to function properly). Misfolded proteins produce more misfolded proteins. Some can cause brain disorders like Alzheimer and Parkinson's disease.[40]

Reasoning and memory also do not function perfectly and on a behavioral level, even "normal" persons do not behave perfectly. Persons with physical or behavioral disorders can be victims of inborn genetic abnormalities. No. Humans are not perfect.

Humans are fallible in ways that were unknown 5 years ago. The findings of recent research could be described as shocking. Humans are not nearly as capable as many suppose or would like to believe. This chapter surveys some current evidence of human fallibility and how it challenges making sense of situations.

Who's in charge, anyway?

Is the conscious mind in charge of the brain, or does the brain have a "mind of its own"? Humans like to believe they are in control of their affairs, but in affairs of the brain, humans actually have limited control. Memory functions are one example.

A widespread belief is that memories recorded in the brain are reasonably accurate and stable. Neither can be relied upon. The initial recording can be distorted and each subsequent memory recall can be further distorted.[41]

A memory is first stored deep within the brain in the hippocampus. This memory also includes important context info, such as its being true or false.[42] But each time the memory is recalled, it is rewritten, and restored, but not without some reprocessing that can distort the memory. Eventually, the memory is moved to the cerebral cortex, but without context memory. Then, a person is unable to remember the context, such as whether it is false or true.[42.]

Also, the brain is selective in what it decides to store or opts to reject. Even before a memory is stored, the information is preprocessed by a biased brain. For instance, the brain has a hard-wired preference for optimistic information and may not even allow storage of something highly pessimistic.[43] This deliberate distortion of reality has profound implications. Imagine an audience listening to a public debate on global warming and climate change. One debater warns of catastrophic climactic consequences. The opposing debater claims there is nothing to worry about because natural processes will cleanse the atmosphere. The information stored by the audience for later recall will heavily favor the optimistic message, whether or not it has merit.

Another example of hard-wired, biased preprocessing is the brain's algorithm for new input that is relevant to previously-stored memory. That algorithm will store information selectively on those parts of the input that most closely agree with the previously-stored memory. Parts of the input that disagree may be censored before storage.[44] Then, the previous memory is updated with the new (censored) information. This kind of biased memory processing also has profound implications. Challenges to old memories are rejected, regardless of merit. Old memories are reinforced, regardless of merit. Old bad ideas can be made worse. Old good ideas may not be made better, because new-sounding proposals can be automatically rejected. The brain will accept a familiar idea (close to previous memory) and reject a new idea (that differs substantially from previous memory)[44]

None of this is good news for making sense of a situation. Not only are information sources unreliable (when depending on memory) but information processing to make sense can also be unreliable. Open-minded, objective reasoning is challenged by distorted memory functions.

Another sober finding of new research is that much of our thinking and behavior in our conscious state is secretly influenced by our subconscious.[45] (The subconscious does not sleep while we are awake.) In other words, we may believe that we are fully in conscious control when we are actually not. For instance, we might be mimicking the behavior of persons nearby without realizing our subconscious is in control. Mimicking behavior can produce both good deeds and misdeeds.[45]

Human fallibility is not limited to unreliable brain functions over which we have no conscious control (as discussed above). Fallibility also extends to brain functions over which we have some control. In the thin line between outward human behavior and internal brain functions, thoughtful control is not 100%. A practical example is road rage. Once a person is engaged in road rage, clear thinking is lost and is difficult to regain. The reasons have to do with body chemistry and how brain functions are divided between different parts of the brain. The explanation is not complicated. The prefrontal cortex (immediately behind the forehead) is the control center for decision-making, concentration, memory retrieval, and other thinking tasks. It also is tasked with keeping emotions in check and prevent primitive impulses from taking charge (such as punching someone in the nose). Actions in road rage are controlled by a different part of the brain tasked for survival and other primitive functions. Called the amygdala (centrally located in the lower brain), it commands release of excessive chemicals under stress situations, like road rage. Those chemicals, such as dopamine and norepinephrine, enable survival actions but also shut down prefrontal cortex functions. In other words, road rage can escalate out of clear-thinking control, while gaining back prefrontal cortex control is unlikely.[46] The result can be unnecessary injury and bloodshed, probably regretted when normal thinking returns.

What does this have to do with making sense? Even mild stress can impair clear thinking.[46] It is just one more example of human fallibility.

This paragraph began with a question: Who's in charge, anyway? When human behavior is under control of the prefrontal cortex, is humanity still fallible? The short answer is yes, as examined in the next paragraph.

Free Will or Keep Will Locked Up?

A play on words but maybe with some meaningful content? The idea of "free will" is, itself, controversial. At least the degree of self-control is debatable. That said, it is clear that humans are fully capable of making choices, deciding between options, making judgments, and formulating opinions. Their being fully capable does not mean the choices, decisions, judgments, and opinions will be well-made or have good results. Results could be quite the opposite, given the handicaps of human fallibility and corrupted information in the public domain. The next paragraph examines human fallibility when the brain's prefrontal cortex is in control of conscious thought.

Believe It or Not

Whether something is believable or not may have nothing to do with truth, reality, facts, hard evidence, etc. It may only have to do with how something is *perceived* by an individual or group. A good example is a crime scene. The real crime scene contains real elements and real events that unfold in real time. The perceived crime scene contains perceived elements and perceived events that unfold in perceived time. Four eyewitnesses to a crime scene can be expected to have four different accounts of the same scene. Eyewitness testimony has earned such an unreliable reputation that its admission as evidence in the courtroom is coming under stricter regulation.[47,48] This departure of perception from reality is an example of human fallibility. "Seeing is believing" is an old and apt saying, but with a very different connotation. Perhaps a better saying would be "Seeing may be misleading." Combining the old and new saying, we might arrive at: "Believing may be misleading."

Michael Shermer, author of *The Believing Brain* (Holt, 2011), asserts: "Once we form beliefs…we maintain and reinforce them through a number of powerful cognitive biases that distort our [perceptions]." Shermer identifies four types of such biases, plus in-group bias (placing greater value to beliefs held by those perceived to be in the same group).[49]

Conscious thought is not a guarantee of objective thought. Deafness to reason appears to afflict the U.S. Congress, whose sharply polarized biases have resulted in legislative gridlock in recent years. Human fallibility is manifested in ways that are unproductive at best and dangerous to democratic society at worst.

Conscious thought can result in self-deception [50] and "motivated reasoning" can lead to distortion of evidence.[51] Religious faith can also impact the reasoning process [52.] and "faith-based belief" is a contemporary concept.

Human fallibility at the conscious level can be so subtle that the conscious mind may be unaware. A specific example might help explain.

In 2008, big gas-guzzling vehicles fell out of favor when gas cost $4/gallon. Many bought new hybrid and electric cars while getting generous tax and refund incentives (which were tied to environmental objectives—the hybrids and electrics chopped toxic emissions). Now, gas is much cheaper. What are the public's priorities? (1) Buying more hybrids and electrics to help meet the Paris climate accord? (2) Buying fewer hybrids and electrics and trading old hybrids and electrics in for gas guzzlers? (3) Buying more gas guzzlers? The answer is (2) + (3)[53.]

Nearly 75% of people who trade in an old hybrid or electric buy an all-gas car (up 18% from 2015). Hybrid and electric sales have dropped to 2.4% of new car sales. Gas-guzzling vehicles are in high demand. Is the nation becoming less environmentally conscious? Not likely. Yet car-buying behavior suggests otherwise. Americans are making choices suggesting fallible judgment. Possibly unconscious fallible judgment?

Disclaimer

This discussion of human fallibility is based on available information on brain functions and human behavior. This information is subject to change as exploratory research continues. What is known on these subjects is infinitesimal compared to what is unknown. This is particularly true of brain research, which is in its infancy. The brain is incredibly complex.

There are 100 billion neurons with 100 trillion connections.[54] How they function together is a puzzle too complex to imagine. By comparison, the nematode worm C. elegans has only 302 neurons and all connections were mapped 20 years ago. Yet it is still a mystery how that simple network functions as a working nervous system.[54] Professor Gary Mavcus of New York University says: "It's not just that we lack answers (on human brains). We don't even agree on the questions."[55]

Section Four: Lack of Constructive Debate

Global warming and climate change have been debated for over 30 years, but with little evidence of significant reconciliation between opposing views. The arguments made 30 years ago are remarkably similar to those heard today. On August 25, 1988, The Seattle Times printed opposing views on the greenhouse effect.[56] One view was expressed by Lester B. Lave, a professor of economics at Carnegie-Mellon University. The opposing view was expressed by Kent Jeffries, a policy analyst on energy and environmental issues at the Heritage Foundation.[56.] Lester Lave expressed concern that greenhouse gases resulting from deforestation and carbon emissions from fossil fuels were "predicted to raise temperatures by perhaps 8 degrees" by the mid-21st century. He acknowledged that "[p]recisely what the result will be is highly uncertain," but argued it would be prudent to begin taking preventive action.[56]

Kent Jeffries asserted the climate proponents were simply wrong. He argued the greenhouse predictions "[were] wrong, or very premature." The current warming trend would probably reverse itself, as it had "many times in the past." He questioned the basis for ordering cutbacks in carbon emissions.[56]

It seems opposing views on climate issues could be narrowed or resolved through constructive debate. Constructive debate, defined here, is face-to-face, interactive debate between issue opponents in which substantive issues are argued. Arguments are supported by valid evidence and debaters occasionally acknowledge merits of their opponents' arguments. Personal attacks are avoided. Reason reigns over passion.

Constructive debate illuminates controversial issues rather than making opinions less open to reconsideration.

These are fine goals, but are strangers to the global warming controversy. Face-to-face, interactive debates are rare. There are "pasted debates" where arguments are pasted into columns labeled “Pro” and “Con”[57] or the text of opposing positions is separated.[58] There have been separate, individual interviews with climate skeptics and proponents which are later aired on television. But traditional face-to-face debates on global warming and climate change are few and far between.

One reason there are so few climate debates could be that such exchanges are frequently unproductive, and often less than civil and objective. One side is generally persuaded by scientific evidence, while the other side is persuaded by beliefs contrary to scientific evidence or perhaps motivated by goals unrelated to evidence or science. The latter group has often been labeled "climate deniers." The chasm between debate sides seems unbridgeable. A debate on the floor of the U.S. Senate in 2008 proved wholly futile.[59] (See Example #2 below). This lack of constructive debate in the global warming controversy might also reflect a muddled situation.

In 1970 (18 years prior to The Seattle Times article), the Clean Air Act was passed by the U.S. Congress to control pollution emissions. However, 10 years’ experience with the environmental regulations spawned sharp divisions between various interest groups.[60.] Industry complained the environmental regulations stifled economic growth. Sound familiar? The climate debate has deep roots and robust persistence. With such a long history, one might hope the debate would have matured and sorted out the issues. Not so. Debate positions seem as entrenched and muddled as in the early days.

To help shed some light on this debate situation, some examples are briefly examined.

Example # 1

Two days before the 1989 anniversary of Earth Day, the opinion page of the New York Times carried side-by-side statements on whether cleaner air was worth the cost.[61] Two U.S. senators on the Environmental Protection sub-committee, Max Baucus and Joseph Lieberman, argued in favor. A professor of environmental science at the University of Virginia, S. Fred Singer, argued against. The opening remarks reveal the depth of division between opposing statements:

In Favor: "The need for a stronger Clean Air Act is as evident as the dirt we breathe. Thanks to the long stalemate on new clean air legislation, smog levels in 1988 were the worst of the decade."

Against: "The potential benefits of clean air bills now before Congress will not be worth the cost imposed on consumers. If history is a guide, politics rather than scientific and health data will determine the eventual legislation."

These opening statements were followed by detailed arguments to support each case. This debate was not interactive or face-to-face. At least good efforts were made to supply credible evidence, which is not always the case in climate debates.

Example # 2

In June 2008, the U.S. Senate was debating climate change. At issue was a Senate bill to cap greenhouse gas emissions and require polluters to purchase permits to emit carbon dioxide.[59] All discussion stopped when Republicans insisted the entire 492-page bill be read by the clerk. This was followed by a near-filibuster monologue by Republican James Inhofe. He was finally interrupted by Democrat Senator John Kerry, who requested Senator Inhofe to yield. Mr. Inhofe refused. After a fourth try, Mr. Kerry blurted, "With all due respect, we are here for a debate. It's hard to debate when you are talking all by yourself."[59] Democrats did have their say at times, but were accused of political theater by Republicans, acknowledging the bill had little chance of being approved. Senator Corker summed it up:

"This bill is going down in flames, as it should. We'll have a real debate about this next year."[59]

Example # 3

Election politics were in full sway in Fall 2010, and climate issues were central where the Tea Party was active. One such place was the State of Indiana. Kelly Khuri, Founder of Clark County Tea Party Patriots, declared: "This so-called climate science is just ridiculous. I think it's all cyclical. Carbon regulation, cap and trade, it's all just a money-control avenue."[62] According to a New York Times/ CBS News poll, more than one-half of Tea Party supporters do not believe global warming will have serious effects any time in the future. Nationwide, 19 Republican candidates for 20 contested Senate seats opposed climate legislation and questioned global warming science.[62] Lisa Denton, founder of We the People of Indiana, asserted: "They're trying to use global warming against the people…It takes away our liberty…Being a strong Christian I cannot help but believe the Lord placed a lot of minerals in our country and it's not there to destroy us."[62]

This example is one side of a climate debate that reveals some of the wide-ranging views of climate skeptics. Other such views that have been heard include: (1) emission reductions will have devastating effects on jobs and the economy, and (2) climate action is a conspiracy to invoke world government and redistribute wealth.

Example # 4

An article in the March 18, 2016 issue of Bulletin of Atomic Scientists focused on the climate positions of four remaining Republicans in the 2016 race for the White House.[63] These four were Ted Cruz, John Kasich, Marco Rubio and Donald Trump. All four had rejected the consensus conclusions of climate science.

Ted Cruz called global warming a "pseudo-scientific theory" which is more religion than science. John Kasich rejected the consensus that "humans are the primary cause of climate change." Marco Rubio agreed with Kasich and does not believe in climate change "in the way these scientists are portraying it." Donald Trump called global warming a hoax and claims it was "created by and for the Chinese."[63]

This example reflects the sorry state of public understanding of global warming and climate change. This is truly remarkable in the year 2016, after decades of IPCC reports, international summit meetings, and public discourse on the issues. It reveals a total disconnect between presidential candidates and potentially the greatest threat to civilization in modern history. The traditional role of public debate in sorting out contemporary issues seems absent in the twenty first century—at least for climate issues.

Example # 5

"The trouble is, on most college campuses there is no debate" is the opening sentence in a short paragraph titled: "The Global Warming Debate on Campus." Published by the National Association of Scholars on September 6, 2011, the statement goes on say students believe the climate issue is "settled" because anyone who does not accept that humans are responsible for climate change "must be a corporate shill or a fool."[64]

This example turned up in an Internet search for climate debates. That search found some instances of "pasted" debates (explained earlier) but no face-to-face, interactive debates between climate opponents. One might expect a likely place to find such debates would be on college campuses. This example claims not so.

Example # 6

An article in Forbes predicted heated debates on climate change in the 2020 U.S. presidential election campaigns, citing the nation's polarization over climate policy.[65] Sixty-four percent of Democrats said that issue would determine who got their vote. That figure was 12% percent for Republicans. Global warming was the third most important issue for Democrats, but only ranked between twenty-third and twenty-ninth for Republicans, according to the Center for Climate Change Communications (Yale and George Mason

Universities). The Forbes article said to expect "important questions being raised about global warming during candidate debates."[65]

Regarding the Forbes prediction about candidate debates, the Democratic National Committee (DNC) declined a proposal to host a debate focused on climate change. Further, the DNC warned "If any candidate participates in climate debates DNC doesn't host, they won't be invited to any future DNC debates. Period." In other words, the DNC was not in favor of climate debates in the 2020 presidential races.

Example # 7

CNN hosted a "Presidential Town Hall" television event on September 4, 2019 to debate the climate crisis in front of a live audience.[66] Ten Democratic Party presidential candidates were invited to reveal their positions on climate change issues and the audience was invited to address questions to the candidates. Each candidate, in turn, presented their positions and answered questions from the audience. There were no exchanges between candidates.

The event was not a debate between candidates, and was hardly constructive in providing closure on any substantive climate issues. Pros and cons on key issues were largely absent.

Example # 8

NBCTV hosted a presidential debate between Donald J. Trump and Joseph R. Biden on October 22, 2020.[67] Twelve minutes were spent on debating climate issues and moderator Kristen Welker urged candidates to focus on solutions in their remarks. Both candidates addressed economic consequences of dealing with the climate crisis or failing to deal with the crisis. They were also asked to consider pollution impacts on communities of color, where many reside near industrial sites.

This was a bona fide debate (albeit brief and narrowly focused). As such, it was a rare event. It was also probably constructive because it helped clarify sharp differences between candidates on the stakes and necessity of reducing carbon emissions. Both political parties seemed happy with the political points scored by their candidates.[67]

These eight examples of climate "debates" are non-typical of traditional debates that drive out PRO/CON positions and challenges between opposing positions. Losers in this situation are "balanced truth" and a public that desires to sort out climate change issues. Another loser is climate consensus, which would facilitate climate action.

Chapter 9 Sources

1. Philip Shabecoff, "Altered Atmosphere a Threat to Earth, New Study Warns," New York Times, January 13, 1986, pp. 1, 6 (I357)
2. Staff, "The Challenge Without Precedent," The Economist, April 25, 2020, pp. 52-53 (I2817)
3. Staff, "The Jigsaw Environment," U.S. News & World Report, December 26, 1988, pp. 92-93 (I463)
4. Philip Shabecoff, "Draft Report on Global Warming Foresees Environmental Havoc in U.S.," New York Times, October 20, 1988, p. 12 (I445)
5. Michael Weisskoph, "U.S. Commits to Talks on 'Greenhouse,'" Washington Post, May 13, 1989, pp. 1, 6 (I499)
6. James Brooke, "For the World's Environmentalists, Obstacles on the Road to Rio," New York Times, March 27, 1992, p. A5 (I625)
7. Edward A. Parson et al., "A Summary of the Major Documents Signed at the Earth Summit and the Global Forum on Environment," Environment, pp.1-5 (I2550)
8. Paul Lewis, "U.N. Panel Finds Action on Environment Lagging," New York Times, May 29, 1994, p. 6 (I729)

9. Barbara Crossett, "Half-Hearted Global Warming Conference Closes Gloomily," New York Times, June 28, 1997, p. 3 (I788)

10. Staff, "Report Card on Rio Summit—Lagging Progress" (approximate title), New York Times, June 17, 1997, p. B14 (I791)

11. William K. Stevens, "Talks on Global Warming End on Pessimist Note", New York Times, November 1, 1997, p. A6 (I800)

12. Justin Gillis, "Panel's Warning on Climate Risk: Worst is to Come," New York Times, March 31, 2014, pp. 1, 3 (I1407)

13. Carol Davenport, "A Climate Accord Based Global Peer Pressure," New York Times, December 15, 2014, p. A3 (I1512)

14. Staff, "3.6 Degrees of Uncertainty," New York Times, December 16, 2014, pp. D1, D3 (I1513)

15. Staff, "Unsustainable Goals," The Economist, March 28, 2015, pp. 63-64 (I1534)

16. Eduardo Porter, "Promises of Climate Change Aid Now Need Money to Back Them Up," New York Times, September 30, 2015, pp. B1, B7 (I1610)

17. Steven E. Koonin, "Tough Realities of the Climate Talks," New York Times, November 4, 2015, p. A27 (I1621)

18. Carol Davenport, "Decision on Climate Rule May Imperil Paris Accord," New York Times, February 11, 2016, p. A18 (I1681)

19. Justin Gillis, Carol Davenport, "Leaders Meet to Sign a Climate Pact Fraught With Uncertainties," New York Times, April 22, 2016, p. A12 (I1738)

20. Carol Davenport, "Climate Pact Negotiators Confront a New Peril", New York Times, November 19, 2016, pp.1, 16 (I1888)

21. Aurelien Breeden et al., "We Are Losing the Battle," New York Times, December 13, 2017, p. A11 (I2166)

22. Staff, "The Great Inaction," The Economist, December 1, 2018, pp. 10, 11 (I2454)

23. Joanna Berendt, "Playing Host to Climate Conference, Poland Promotes Coal," New York Times, December 5, 2018, p. A8 (I2460)

24. Brad Plumer, Lisa Friedman, "Trump Has Allies on Fossil Fuels," New York Times, December 11, 2018, pp. 1, 12 (I2466)

25. Somini Sengupta, "New Targets For Emissions Fall Far Short of Paris Goals," New York Times, February 27, 2021, p. A9 (I3022)

26. Michael Shermer, "The Science of Lying," Scientific American, April, 2014, p. 87 (I1411)

27. Staff, "Stemming the Tide of Fake Medicines" New York Times, May 18, 2015, p. A16 (I1559)

28. William K. Rashbaum, "Inspector's Faked Tests May Be 'Tip of the Iceberg,'" New York Times, April 27, 2010, A17 (I1163)

29. Jacques Steinberg, "Writer's Work in USA Today is Called False," New York Times, March 20, 2004, pp 1, 11 (I 920)

30. Eric Lipton "U.S. Test Finds Passport Fraud is Going Unseen," New York Times, June 29, 2005, pp. 1, 19 (I962)

31. Paul Krugman, "'Swift Boating' the Planet," New York Times, May 29, 2006, p. A19 (I991)

32. Declan Walsh, "Fake Diplomas, Real Cash: A Net of Made-up Schools," New York Times, May 18, 2015, pp. 1, 6 (I1558)

33. Christine Haughney, "A High Flier in Real Estate is Sentenced," New York Times, September 21, 2010, p. A23 (I1201)

34. Lee Wasserman, Exxon's Climate Change Deceit," New York Times, October 23, 2019, p. A27 (I2778)

35. Ian Urbina, "Inspector General's Inquiry Faults Actions of Federal Drilling Regulators," New York Times, May 25, 2010 (I1177)

36. Rebecca R. Ruiz, "Four Cancer Charities are Accused of Fraud," New York Times, May 20, 2015, pp. B1, B2 (I1560)

37. David Streitfield, "For $2 a Star, an On-line Retailer gets 5-Star Product Reviews," New York Times, Jan. 27, 2012, p. A1 (I1292)

38. Carl M. Cannon, "UnTruth & Consequences," The Atlantic, January/February, 2007, pp. 56-67 (I1015)

39. Hiroko Tabuchi, "Climate Denial Infuses Reports of U.S. Agency," New York Times, March 2, 2020, pp. 1, 21 (I2805)

40. Staff, "Chain Reaction," The Economist, September 12, 2015, pp. 74-75 (I1604)

41. Christopher Chabris, Daniel Simons, "Why Our Memory Fails Us" New York Times, December 2, 2014, p. A23 (I1503)

42. Sam Wang, Sandra Aamodt, "Your Brain Lies to You," New York Times, June 27, 2008, p. A19 (I1089)

43. Tali Sharot, "Major Delusions," New York Times, May, 14, 2011, pp. 1-3 (I1244)

44. Merim Bilalic, Peter McLeod, "Why Good Thoughts Block Better Ones," Scientific American, March, 2014, pp. 75-79 (I1401)

45. John A. Bargh, "Our Unconscious Mind," Scientific American, January 2014, pp 30-37 (I1392)

46. Amy Arnsten et al., "This is Your Brain in Meltdown," Scientific American, April, 2012, pp. 50-53 (I1307)

47. Benjamin Weiser, "New Jersey Jurors to be Warned About Reliability of Eyewitness Identification," New York Times, July 20, 2012 (I1331)

48. Editors, "A Check on Bad Eyewitness Identifications," New York Times, December 6, 2012, p. A26 (I1347)

49. Michael Shermer, "The Believing Brain," Scientific American, July, 2011 p. 85 (I1255)

50. Robert Trivers, "The Folly of Fools: The Logic of Deceit & Self Deception in Human Life" (book excerpt), Scientific American, Nov. 11, 2011, p. 92 (I1283)

51. Michael Shermer, "Logic-Tight Compartments," Scientific American, January 2013, p. 77 (I1355)

52. Staff, "Faith & Reason," The Economist, February 22, 2014, p. 28 (I1398)

53. Richtel, Matt, "Car Buyers Pulling the Plug," New York Times, June 28, 2016, pp. D1, D2 (I1771)

54. Carl Zimmer, "100 Trillion Connections," Scientific American, January, 2011, pp. 59-63 (I1226)

55. Gary Marcus, "The Trouble With Brain Science," New York Times, July 12, 2014, p. A17 (I1451)

56. Lester B. Lave, Kent Jeffreys, "Greenhouse Effect: Two Views," Seattle Times, July 25, 1988, p. A7 (I429)

57. Staff, "Climate Change Controversies," The Royal Society, June 6, 2019, pp. 1-12, (I2552)

58. Staff, "Background of the Issue," PRO/CON.org, June 28, 2016, pp.1-6 (I1974)

59. David M. Heriszenhorn, "More Talking Than Listening in Senate Debate About Climate Change," New York Times, June 5, 2008, p. A19 (I1085)

60. Staff, "Clean Air Debate," U.S. News & World Report, October 19, 1981, pp. 46-47 (I142)

61. Max Baucus, Joseph I. Lieberman, "Clean Air Worth the Cost," New York Times, April 22, 1989, p. 15 (I490)

62. John M. Broder, "Skepticism on Climate Change is Article of Faith for Tea Party," New York Times, October 21, 2010, pp. 1, 4 (I1214)

63. Richard C. J. Sommerville, Catherine Gautier, "Climate Change & 2016 Election," Bulletin of the Atomic Scientists, March 13, 2016, pp. 1-4 (I1701)

64. George Leef, "The Global Warming Debate on Campus," National Association of Scholars, September 6, 2011 (I2551)

65. Hersh Shefrin, "Get Ready as Climate Change Debate Will Go Mainstream in 2020 Presidential Election Campaign," Forbes, May 27, 2019, pp. 1-4 (I2554)

66. Staff, "Presidential Town Hall: Climate Debate" (D.C. Whitmore notes), CNN TV, September 4, 2019 (I2647)

67. Lisa Friedman, "Debate Puts New Focus on Climate," New York Times, October 24, 2020, pp. 1, 13 (I2913)

Chapter 10: Situation Assessment and Conclusions

Principal Assessment

Climate threats, including the ways they are likely to intensify in the future, are widely underestimated. This means the magnitude and gravity of the climate crisis are generally misunderstood. This crisis is currently out of control, and it is accelerating towards potentially unstoppable disasters (such as extreme coastal flooding, mass starvation, severe droughts with fresh water shortages, genocidal plagues, economic panics, and expanding poverty). The habitat of all life forms is at risk. Species extinction is already underway.

Emissions are still growing, global fossil fuel demand is accelerating, and new emission sources are still being discovered. Geo-engineering schemes to suck pollutants out of the atmosphere or block sunlight (still unproven) might never reduce cumulative emissions before tipping points are reached. Such mitigation might never be cost-effective. Disastrous scenarios can probably be minimized only if carbon emission rates are promptly and substantially reduced.

2019 was the second hottest year on record, and 2015–2019 was warmer than any 5-year period in the last 140 years. (Note: Information in Chapter 10 is drawn from previous chapters, where sources of information are listed.)

Climate change and its impacts are accelerating. The future growth of the climate threat will likely be driven by two major social movements: the rapid growth of the global urban population and the industrial revolution in the developing world. These movements create expanding demand for energy generation and consumption, causing still more greenhouse gas emissions. Emissions from the cement industry are one example.

Aside from new emissions resulting from the social movements noted above, additional greenhouse gas emissions will result from rising atmospheric and ocean temperatures releasing frozen carbon deposits. Thawing permafrost is one example. The cumulative result from all emission sources could be a carbon emissions surge that might end the possibility of reducing global emissions to zero in the foreseeable future. The odds and disastrous impacts of such an emissions surge increase the longer that significant dependency on fossil fuels continues.

Examples of climate threats are rising sea levels, receding glaciers, deforestation, leaks from natural gas infrastructure, thawing permafrost, thawing marine carbon reserves, the frequency and severity of robust pandemics (e.g., COVID-19), the devastation of marine life, and climate and weather extremes. Some threat components have accelerating growth due to self-amplifying dynamics, aka "vicious cycles."

Society's efforts to combat climate threats lack consensus, urgency, detailed action plans and committed resources. Global action is not on a scale to match the gravity of the situation. Climate disasters continue to grow in frequency and intensity. The climate threat is approaching tipping points, while society is not responding in crisis mode. Technology solutions are not being pursued with urgent, crisis-level priority (24/7).

Principal Conclusions

One. Climate threat components consist of:

(a) Cumulative climate severity (sum of all threat types—extreme weather, sea level rise, pandemics, economic threats, etc.).

(b) Threat intensification:

- (1) Stable dynamics: linear, non-linear (exponential)
- (2) Unstable dynamics: self-amplification (vicious cycle)
- (3) A potential carbon emissions surge made more likely and destructive by continued energy dependency on fossil fuels.

(c) Multiple tipping points, both suspected and unknown.

Two. The combination of all threat components poses unacceptable risks to humans and other lifeforms. This climate situation is an immediate crisis—perhaps the greatest crisis ever.

Three. The root cause of post-industrial climate threats is global warming. Threat escalation is worsened by increased global heating. Global warming must be slowed and reversed as soon as possible to minimize climate threats and enable progress towards climate security.

Four. Immediate, crisis-level global climate action on a scale matching cumulative climate threats is required to begin controlling global warming as soon as possible.

Five. An appropriate and achievable climate action goal is to reach zero human-caused carbon emissions by 2035 or earlier.

Six. Currently available and emerging technologies are sufficient to achieve zero emissions by 2035 when coupled with crisis-level global action and adequate funding.

Seven. International entities and national governments have failed to mount climate action on a scale and with an urgency equivalent to the cumulative climate threat. Their efforts must immediately be strongly augmented by the private sector (including private individuals).

Eight. Ad hoc, "business-as-usual" climate action is not reducing total carbon emissions and is unable to keep pace with growing climate threats. Crisis-level global action requires project-based, detailed planning and 24/7 project scheduling. Private sector leadership is needed to organize and execute an integrated, coordinated action plan.

Nine. Adequate funding to support the climate action goal of zero human-caused carbon emissions by 2035 or earlier can be secured through long-term bonds and other sources. Bond redemption can be assisted by a for-profit energy services global corporation.

Discussion

Discussion begins after a statement concerning the carbon emissions surge possibility discussed in Chapter 2.

Society has an urgent and pivotal decision to make. What it decides in the next one or two years will likely determine whether climate change proceeds on a path towards unprecedented human catastrophes and chronic misery or a path towards climate security and a hopeful future. The choice is between a three-step global action: (1) immediately begin slashing carbon emissions at least 10% per year, (2) fully abandoning fossil fuel energy by 2035 and (3) aggressively replacing polluting energy with 100% clean energy OR continuing the current dependency on polluting energy for the indefinite future. Chapter 11 outlines a comprehensive and timely plan to implement the clean energy goal.

The stakes are between a carbon emissions surge that might be largely avoidable and one that is probably close to inevitable. Such a carbon emissions surge would likely end practical hopes for reducing emissions to near zero before the most extreme climate disasters become unstoppable.

Are the assertions made above absolutely certain? No. The climate situation is riddled with uncertainties and unknowns. Little, if anything, about the climate is absolutely certain -- including the survival of civilization in a worsening environment. Whether society acknowledges it or not, the global community is faced with making a critical decision in the midst of uncertainties and unknowns. Risks of action should be weighed against risks of inaction, as guided by common sense and rational reasoning.

This is the fifth decade that society has been avoiding a full commitment to crisis-level global climate action. Calls for such action began in the 80's. Scientists are now warning that time is running out to avoid environmental calamities. Now is the time for society to prove it is civilized and make an explicit decision, rather than it being decided by the default of inaction.

This is the end of statement and beginning of the discussion.

The Principal Assessment began with an assertion that "Climate threats are widely underestimated." Climate change impacts and threats are discussed in Chapters 1 and 4-7. Not sufficiently emphasized is how human-caused global warming has added new and more severe climate threats to Earth's environment. Such a discussion here might help in understanding the current and evolving threat situation.

Severe weather is not new to the 20th and 21st centuries, but its greater frequency and intensity is the result of human-caused global warming of the atmosphere and oceans. This is because higher temperatures (1) create more opportunities (enabling conditions) to catalyze severe weather and (2) they provide more energy to fuel severe weather growth into monster storms. More frequent and intense severe weather is more damaging (costly) and more deadly than that in pre-industrial times. Those added damages and fatalities must be understood as the result of human-caused global warming.

More frequent and intense severe weather does not necessarily involve new natural processes. New kinds of climate threats (enabled by global warming) likely tap into dormant natural processes. A current example is thawing permafrost (explained in Chapter 4). Before global warming there was no significant, large-scale thawing in recent history. Today, large-scale permafrost thawing has begun, and decomposition of organic matter is releasing greenhouse gases (GHG) into the atmosphere.

This carbon release will likely set-up self-amplifying cycles that greatly accelerate GHG emissions (see Chapter 4). As this activity expands across permafrost regions, it is conceivable that a tipping point would be reached which renders the thawing/GHG emissions cycle unstoppable. In other words, thawing/soil decomposition could continue until virtually all permafrost has melted and the entire stored carbon deposit becomes destined for release into the atmosphere. Of course, unfettered global warming would be a partner to that climate calamity. Earth's habitat could suffer catastrophic losses. Societal intervention by quickly bringing human-caused carbon emissions to a halt would likely increase odds that a tipping point event could be preempted.

Large-scale rainforest removal (for agricultural or other purposes) is a new threat in the global warming era. It has a similar effect as permafrost thawing (adding carbon to the environment) but involves different means: radical reduction of natural carbon sinks. There was no such rainforest threat in pre-industrial times.

A third new climate threat is increasing sea levels caused by melting polar ice and mountain glaciers. The melt is not new, but the scale and unstoppable nature are new and are attributable to global warming. Current increases in sea level are slight, but are tragic for coastal communities already displaced by the encroaching seas.

A growing concern is accelerated polar melting from unusually warm ocean currents. The planet's oceans have absorbed 93% of the added heat from global warming. The possibility of tipping points and glaciers sliding en masse into the ocean cannot be discounted. One glacier of immediate concern is Thwaites Glacier in Antarctica, which could quickly add 11 feet to sea levels (Chapter 1).

A total melt down of polar ice and mountain glaciers is now conceivable, which was not the case before the 19th Century. If all polar ice were to melt, then sea levels would increase over 200 feet. Even if that catastrophe did not happen soon, it would someday impact generations not far removed from persons living today. Even one-half that sea level rise would be profoundly devastating to the global economy and to the planet's habitat. Blame goes to global warming and human-caused carbon emissions.

A fourth type of new climate threat is recently discovered marine carbon deposits held in the ocean by hydrate caps or under seabed permafrost. These may be prone to tipping point events. Researchers suspect some of these large carbon reservoirs may be near the point of thawing and releasing GHG. How many such carbon deposits are in the oceans and how big are they? Answers are currently unknown but expanded sensor surveys should be on the climate action to-do list. There was no such threat before the Industrial Age, because global warming was apparently necessary to enable threat conditions.

A fifth type of new climate threat is the economic consequences of cascading and multiple climate disasters that exceed the capacity of financial institutions to cope with losses (see Chapter 7). The economic consequences of climate disasters are not new: what is new is the prospect of cumulative and massive defaults that would bring down the very foundation of global financial infrastructures. The resulting economic chaos might exceed that of a deep global depression. This is a new climate threat that has no known historical precedent.

Other climate impacts (described in Chapters 5-7) in the unprecedented future could include record-breaking wildfires, extreme droughts with severe fresh water shortages, multiple economic panics with expanding poverty, rampaging pandemics and widespread starvation.

Another assertion in the Principal Assessment was that "Society's efforts to combat climate threats lack consensus, urgency, detailed action plans and committed resources. Global action is not on a scale to match the gravity of the situation." Beginning with the last sentence, the gravity of the situation is addressed in the chapters on climate threats (1,4,6 and 7) and in the threats discussion preceding this paragraph.

Climate goals without detailed plans for achieving those goals have little practical value. Plans without resources to implement them also have limited value. When goals are without a global social consensus decision to enforce them, then detailed plans and resource commitments are meaningful only for local, regional, and national climate goals. In that case, a secure global social future is in jeopardy and Earth's habitat is at risk.

This chapter's situation assessment reveals that society lacks meaningful consensus on how to cope with global warming and climate change. There is a dangerous mismatch between (1) the great magnitude and urgency of climate threats and (2) weak, untimely climate goals. This current mismatch also stands to block the path to a secure climate future. It follows that if global society fails to implement adequately scaled climate action goals, then a profoundly grim future becomes more likely.

It should be noted that no nation on the planet is entirely safe from climate threats until all nations are safe. Stated differently, the climate fate of one nation depends upon climate behaviors across the globe. This situation stems from the fact that all nations share the one and only biosphere. Atmospheric and ocean circulation have no respect for national borders.

Like it or not, climate action success must be on a global scale. It follows that crisis-level climate action plans and projects must be on a global scale. This is one reason why climate action should be led by the private sector, with support and coordination from governments.

Society is still near square one in knowing what the future holds for comprehensive, crisis-scale climate action. Prospects for bringing global warming under control are currently unknown beyond casual speculation and disjointed efforts to trim greenhouse gas emissions. Air pollution levels continue to climb, as do global temperatures.

Scientists warn time is running out. They also advise that near-term efforts provide leverage in lowering long-term risks. Continued delay can magnify future climate disasters. Concerted action to slash emissions should begin immediately, followed by expedited replacement of carbon fuel energy with non-polluting energy. Specific remedies are proposed in Chapter 11.

Problems with the "net-zero" climate goal concept.

This chapter would not be complete without discussing why the "net-zero" concept is not retained in defining an appropriate carbon emission goal. This concept is fraught with problems, as discussed below:

First, the net-zero goal is license to pollute until and beyond 2050. By definition, it only requires pollution emissions to be balanced by efforts to reduce emissions. Carbon emissions beyond 2050 are presumed to be acceptable as long as they are balanced by efforts to reduce emissions. Pollution emissions could continue to 2075, 2100, or even later. There is no end date for pollution emissions to finally top out. Also, "efforts to reduce emissions" lack definition, accountability and transparency. “Balance” may be more theoretical than actual.

Second, there is no guarantee that emission reduction efforts will actually offset pollution emissions. Consequently, this has the appearance of a giant loophole to avoid any real control over pollution emissions or any halt to expanding fossil fuel consumption.

Third, there are supposed offsets that provide no actual reductions in carbon emissions to compensate for the allowed pollution. An example of a phony offset would be an investment in geo-engineering research that provided no practical technology to significantly reduce carbon in the environment. Any such investment would not be a real offset even though it might be acceptable under net-zero rules.

Fourth, there are delayed offsets that become real reductions in environmental carbon long after the permitted pollution has been absorbed in the environment. An example of such delayed offsets is tree planting that becomes an effective carbon sink some 30–40 years after the saplings are planted. Unfortunately, the climate damage resulting from the allowed pollution would have been done long before the carbon sinks matured. Catastrophic tipping points might also have been encountered in the interim. Such delayed offsets have negative value in achieving urgent climate goals because the permitted pollution has already worsened climate change before the offset becomes effective.

Other problems are that the net-zero concept delays the zero emissions solution, increases risks of unstoppable climate change, and causes more species extinction than the zero emissions solution.

Finally, the net-zero concept is usually married to an untimely goal of 2050. This means the zero emissions solution would have to wait until sometime after 2050. Conclusions#2 and#3 above stipulate that the crisis situation requires slowing global warming "soon as possible." The year 2035 is estimated to be the soonest that human-caused carbon pollution can be virtually ended (though an earlier date should be targeted, and 24/7 project scheduling might make that feasible).

A positive goal in combating global warming is to move towards a situation less threatening and unpredictable. The name given to that situation is "global climate security". The term is defined below:

Global climate security is a stable state of climate that is non-threatening and is advantageous for humanity and all other life forms.

Global warming has disrupted a relatively stable climate that had prevailed for about 1,000 years. That disruption has led to a situation in which climate is no longer predictable with the confidence that was enjoyed in recent history. Return to global climate security should be a goal in combating global warming. Climate security would be a positive goal worth pursuing.

Reaching the goal of global climate security would likely follow a trajectory passing through a series of intermediate objectives. Making that happen would require practical plans and commitment to those plans by society at large.

It should be remembered the world community rose to the threat of thinning ozone over the poles. Despite uncertainties about future impacts, there was global consensus that risks had to be matched by effective action. Collective action was taken and ozone thinning was at least temporarily arrested. This is a success story to remember in considering the way forward to turning back the threats associated with global warming.

With that thought in mind, this chapter takes an "off-ramp" from the gloom of climate threats and the less-than-satisfactory response by society to those threats. Coming up is Chapter 11 and an "on- ramp" to reasons for optimism. The following paragraph concludes this chapter:

Chapter 10 is about the current reality of the climate change situation, which includes how climate threats are likely to evolve if not mitigated. A much better future outlook is within reach. Society can move decisively forward by engaging global warming in a fight to win. Then, prospects for the future are viewed as exceptionally rich in opportunities to chart a path towards global climate security and lay a foundation for future progress.

Chapter 11: Remedies for the Climate Change Situation

Reasons for Optimism

This chapter focuses on solutions and climate action objectives, providing a basis for optimism that society can begin moving toward a climate future that is more anticipated than feared. Reasons for optimism begin with the fact that crisis-level climate action must become much more aggressive and expansive to counter the unprecedented array of climate threats. Recent calls for expedited climate action include a new report from the Intergovernmental Panel on Climate Change (IPCC)[11, 12] Answering such calls for urgent and crisis-scaled climate action would bring with it new hope and new promise. This new climate challenge could also be rewarding on several levels, ranging from personal to global. For example, national sovereigns should expect to benefit from increased national security.

Reasons for optimism can be seen in the conclusions listed in Chapter 10. Crisis-level climate action requires a shift from ad hoc, "business-as-usual" activity to detailed and coordinated action plans with 24/7 project scheduling. This shift might be likened to an urgent conversion from a peacetime environment to a global wartime environment (not experienced in the U.S. and Europe since World War II). The objective is not just to combat global warming, but to win as soon as possible. Winning the first battle is ending human-caused carbon emissions by 2035 or earlier. The climate crisis is immediate, so the shift to crisis-level climate action must be expedited. Business operations in the private sector are accustomed to making rapid adjustments, which is another reason to look at the private sector for leadership. The private sector also understands how to organize and secure funding for a new effort or enterprise.

A "first battle" was mentioned above. Are there other battles? Yes, because there are still severe climate threats to counter in addition to the objective of ending pollution emissions. One concern is lack of scientific data needed to monitor and evaluate climate threats (such as polar ice melting, thawing permafrost, and marine carbon deposits). Collection of these data can be both difficult and dangerous. Data collection involves placing sensors in environments that are often hostile and where access can be difficult to impossible. It may be necessary to develop special robotic equipment, including drones and aquatic platforms, to install and maintain the needed sensors. Such equipment could be developed and tested at a crisis-level research and development (R&D) center proposed in next section.

In any case, a project to collect the necessary scientific data requires battling the elements. Analysis of collected data would advance scientific understanding and modeling of the various climate threats, which would aid efforts to monitor and counter those threats.

Another "battle" example is to save coral reefs from continuing assaults from warming oceans. There are some successful rescue efforts, but these are extremely tedious, labor-intensive and costly. Such efforts need to be greatly expanded and continued to assure that compromised coral reefs will survive.

Still another battle example is an attempt to disrupt or neutralize "vicious cycle" dynamics associated with carbon emissions from thawing permafrost (Chapter 4). Potential remedies would need to be researched, but one possibility might be chemical intervention to interfere with the soil decomposition process. Alternatively, a brute force approach might be scraping decomposing soil into scattered mounds, then capping localized emissions. Any remedy is bound to be an expensive and long battle, but probably necessary to enable climate security in the foreseeable future.

These examples of crisis-level projects are not yet being contemplated because society has not raised its horizons to effectively counter such climate threats. When such projects are undertaken, they will add credence to climate optimism.

Crisis-Level Climate Action (CLCA)

Another basis for increased optimism are technology initiatives pursued under crisis-level climate action (CLCA). First, clean energy technologies now being developed and implemented by developed nations (wind, solar, etc.) can be deployed in developing nations lacking that technology. This climate action objective is discussed at length later in this chapter.

Second, research and development (R&D) of all climate-related technologies can be pursued on a much more concerted level than the assorted efforts now scattered across the globe. Four major R&D centers (one for each of the four global quadrants) are envisioned to spearhead the projects most critical to CLCA. These centers would be sited on campuses with amenities allowing for 24/7 self-sufficiency (residential housing, city services, utilities, etc.). Technical work would be continuous and be supported by office facilities, meeting rooms, large auditoria, laboratories, machine shops, staffed computer facilities, central tool and instrument supplies, mock-up buildings, instrumented test fields, environmental chambers, comfort lounges, food services, and other resources that enable expedited product design, development and testing. Technical consultations across project boundaries would utilize the full potential of all resident skills and specialties. As in the Manhattan Project development of the atomic bomb, all-hands brainstorming in the auditorium can help keep stalled projects moving. These fully-equipped, high-capacity R&D facilities could support all the climate battles, and would also add credence to climate optimism.

Continuing the discussion of technology initiatives...

A little over an hour's drive east of Seattle's metropolitan area are the world-famous apple orchards of eastern Washington. Something else is growing in a former orchard that happens to be related to the global climate crisis. In spring 2021, there was a groundbreaking for an "electrolyzer" that splits H_2O molecules to produce 100% clean hydrogen fuel.[1] This electrolyzer will be powered by excess electricity from a hydroelectric dam on the nearby Columbia River. The clean hydrogen (also called green hydrogen) can power a fuel cell to produce electricity—just like on the International Space Station and other space systems!! The *only* chemical byproduct of fuel cell operations is pure water—nothing toxic or polluting.

Cars, trucks, and other transportation conveyances can be powered by hydrogen. So can industrial furnaces, home furnaces, and almost anything else. Hydrogen is a clean fuel that can be burned but does not emit carbon pollution. Daimler, builder of Freightliner heavy trucks, has made the strategic decision to switch from diesel to hydrogen fuel for its heavy trucks. This change offers buyers lower purchase and operating costs.[2] The environment will benefit from replacement of carbon emissions with carbon-free emissions.

A worldwide switch from fossil fuels to carbon-free hydrogen would be an enormous undertaking—but a necessary objective for crisis-level climate action (CLCA). A candidate name for this objective could be "The Hydrogen Initiative," and this could be the core business of the for-profit global corporation mentioned in Chapter 10's Principal Conclusions. A generic name for this corporation could be "Global Hydrogen Services Corporation" (GHSC).

A May 18, 2021 Special Report of the International Energy Agency (IEA) states hydrogen use is expected to expand rapidly after 2030, with across-the-board end-use consumption. These uses include electricity, refineries, buildings, agriculture, transport, and industry.[3] This report further estimates there will be "15 million hydrogen fuel cell vehicles on the road by 2030."[3] Clearly, hydrogen is "The Fuel of the Future."

One of the more challenging hydrogen applications might be aviation. However, Airbus plans to build a zero-emissions aircraft by 2035.[4, 5] Three different design configurations all feature a hybrid combination of hydrogen-powered turbines and hydrogen fuel cells supplying electricity.[5] Fuel cells with the same power output as batteries have half the weight and are quicker to recharge. Aviation and automotive fuel cells development could be projects of the CLCA R&D centers discussed earlier. The global market for efficient hydrogen aviation fuel should be enormous as society seeks alternatives to fossil-fuel-powered commercial aircraft.

Hydrogen power applications are bound to multiply as H_2 production and distribution expand. Costs are certain to decline sharply as hydrogen uses multiply. Steel-making in northern Sweden is one application benefiting from abundant hydrogen availability.[6] A paste form of hydrogen has also been developed that looks promising for small-powered applications such as scooters.[7]. California is one place where a hydrogen economy is being promoted.[8]These are modest beginnings in a trend that should grow quickly as society continues to seek non-polluting solutions.

Hydrogen has become the leading candidate for replacing fossil fuels.[13] Recent advances in hydrogen fuel technology have been spurred by economies (such as those in Europe) desiring to be independent from Russia's oil and gas. Also, the existing natural gas infrastructure is seen as an important asset to facilitate the shift to hydrogen fuel.

The costs of making clean hydrogen are expected to tumble with new investments and new methods.[13] Key technology initiatives are also finding ways to join hydrogen production with other clean power sources such as wind and solar. Hydrogen's energy storage capability makes it a good companion.[13]

Solar and wind power growth have benefitted from subsidies, as have electric and hybrid automotive sales. Subsidies for hydrogen power would boost its competitiveness with fossil fuels, and should be considered a CLCA priority.

Hydrogen power technology is maturing at an important moment in the midst of the growing climate crisis. Perhaps it is a "good tipping point" that can catapult society towards global climate security. In any case, hydrogen fuel is a viable replacement for fossil fuels. This is reason enough for credible optimism in the future.

Organizing for Climate Action

Crisis-Level Climate Action (CLCA) is a good moniker for identifying what is needed to combat global warming, but it is appropriate to give a name to the organization that would be responsible for planning and executing CLCA. That organization should have the option of choosing its own name, but a preliminary name can be the "Climate Project Administration" (CPA). The CPA should also have the option of describing its mission and how it will organize to accomplish that mission. However, it might be helpful in the beginning to have some provisional ideas. The following paragraphs offer some tentative thoughts.

The CPA's principal mission would be to end society's energy dependence on fossil fuels by 2035 or earlier. A longer-term objective would be to facilitate actions that counter climate threats and result in a global state of climate security (as defined in Chapter 10). The organization would be intended to augment and support current efforts to reduce global carbon emissions. It would further be intended to expand on those current efforts and aggressively counter climate change threats (as described in this book).

CPA is envisioned as a private-sector (non-government) entity managed by volunteer officials. These officials would be drawn from a candidate pool of qualified professionals certified by a human resources department within CPA. CPA, and all affiliate groups would operate on a 24/7 schedule until the primary mission is accomplished.

A separate board of governors would govern during each 8-hour shift. Each of these three boards would seat 16 governors, drawn from 4 different sources (each having 4 different Board tenures), as follows:

Governor Sources (4 each)	**Board Tenures** per Source
Government officials Industry executives Foundation/NGO officials Citizens-at-large	1 Yr. 2 Yrs. 3 Yrs. 4 Yrs.

Governors that have served one term would be eligible to rejoin the Candidate Pool after a 4-year absence from the Board. This is one example of a Board policy that might be adopted by Board vote. Three additional examples are quorum level (11?); Board officers (Chair, Vice Chair, Secretary?) and annual governor compensation (a nominal level of $150K?).

Early CPA activities might include: (1) defining CPA operating policies and organizational structure; (2) filling top executive positions; (3) deciding funding strategies and initiating fund drives; (4) outlining specific CPA project objectives; (5) starting the bidding process for R&D center site selection; (6) beginning recruitment for key non-executive positions; and (7) beginning establishment of for-profit global corporation to plan, design and execute a global hydrogen infrastructure. A tentative name for this corporation is "Global Hydrogen Energy Services (GHES). Headquarters for CPA and GHES could be located within one of the R&D campuses.

Each CPA governor would be assigned office facilities to accommodate their executive suite and personally selected staff. One potential function for the governor and staff could be inspector general of one or more CPA projects. The CPA would have other checks and balances within its operations, including overlapping means of transparency. The CPA would likely be controlling exceptionally large amounts of funds. Transparency and checks and balances would enhance confidence that CPA funds were under control.

CPA climate actions would be executed under specific projects led by project managers. CPA projects would be highly focused and tightly scheduled as broken out of a CPA objective. An example of a CPA objective would be to build manufacturing plants for producing hydrogen. Examples of three CPA projects under that objective would be to (1) purchase or lease land for each plant; (2) produce a common design for the plant structure; and (3) obtain all necessary permits from local jurisdictions.

Central project control would be provided by a project control center (PCC) located in or near CPA headquarters. PCC would operate 24/7 and function much like a space control center, with current status displays and controller stations. This capability would provide real-time access to the precise status of each CPA project. As needs or problems arose, CPA management could respond quickly to maintain overall momentum of climate actions.

Costs and Funding of Climate Action

How much will climate action cost, and how will that cost be paid? Those two questions need to be considered separately, because each question raises more questions.

Beginning with the cost of climate action, this answer depends on how some other questions are answered. For example, what is the time period over which costs are accumulated? Another question: What specific climate actions are included? Still another question: In what nations or regions of the globe are costs being accumulated?

In the discussion to this point, climate action has been divided between activity before and after 2035 (when the primary mission has been accomplished). Activity after 2035 has been described as "battles" against remaining climate threats. Cost estimation might as well be divided the same way. However, the mission goal has been defined as 2035 or earlier. So, instead of defining an end date for the first cost estimation period, it can be defined as the end of the primary mission.

The next question has to do with specific actions to be included for cost estimation. This has been answered to some extent by (1) description of reasons for optimism; (2) early CPA activities listed above; (3) thoughts on the enormous undertaking of switching from fossil fuels to hydrogen fuels;

(4) technology initiatives, including four R&D centers; (5) examples given of post-2035 battles; (6) establishment of the GHES corporation; and (7) establishment of the CPA board and headquarters.

Another specific activity mentioned earlier in this chapter is helping developing nations implement the wind and solar technologies now being implemented by developed nations. That help is envisioned as CPA supplying and installing the systems (such as off-shore wind farms). Also envisioned is CPA providing hydrogen fuel infrastructures at the same time. This climate action should include India, Africa, Indonesia, and perhaps elsewhere. This will be a very high-cost endeavor. It will also be extremely important to the success of crisis-level climate action, because these nations are now headed towards dependency on new, coal-fired power plants. In the case of India, this fact was explained in Chapter 2.[9,10,11] The cost of this clean energy assistance to developing nations is bound to be in the trillions of dollars but these costs can be recovered over the long term from utility costs paid by energy consumers.

While we are on this subject, the positive benefits to the grantors of this assistance should be summarized. This assistance can be considered an energy systems investment and benefits then count as returns on investment. The greatest return is probably the saving of grantor lives and disaster costs from reducing the severity of climate catastrophes that would have resulted from increased carbon emissions (had clean power not replaced polluting power). Recipient nations' populations and dollars would also be saved (as well as those of all other nations not even involved in CPA's assistance to developing nations).

Another source of returns would come from ownership in the electric utilities that were installed freely. Users of supplied electricity would be billed monthly. Rates would be negotiated with recipient nations (which would receive a percentage of revenues). That investment would grow with the expansion of the population and economy. At some point, the entire investment would be fully repaid, and future earnings could then be reinvested in the local economy. In other words, this would be a win-win solution to the clean power situation for all parties involved.

Moving on to estimating the costs of post-2035 battles, it seems that activity is overwhelmed with uncertainties (including the number of battles and how long each would last). It also seems this activity would be necessary no matter what the cost. Perhaps this is a situation where cost is not much an issue. It should also be remembered that investments made in winning climate battles would save untold trillions of dollars in climate disaster losses that were prevented.

Moving on to the last question, what parts of the globe will be included for cost accumulation? Probably the best answer is wherever CPA has provided assistance, which could be anywhere on the globe.

Following this attempt to answer the prerequisite questions, the total climate action cost can now be addressed. However, another question has surfaced: Are profits from investments to be subtracted from estimated costs? That is a good question and one to leave hanging.

The total cost of crisis-level climate action (before and after 2035) is crudely estimated at "many trillions." Much of that investment might be eventually recovered (perhaps even exceeded someday as net profit). The cost discussion is now closed.

Funding of crisis-level climate action is the next topic for discussion. Initial funding needs will be rather modest, as it will take months of organizing efforts before the CPA is in a position to launch a significant number of climate action projects. Seed money to establish legal entities, launch a founding organization and plan fundraising is the first need. The private sector is a likely source for such funds (perhaps private individuals and/or foundations).

As mentioned in Chapter 10's Principal Conclusions, the main source of funds is expected to be long-term bonds. That conclusion is subject to revision by the founding organization when fundraising is planned. The rationale behind long- term bonds is that climate action is bound to need the use of funds for a long time before funds can be returned to investors. A model for such bonds is the U.S. Savings Bonds program, which helped fund the nation's role in World War II. Those savings bonds helped bridge the long gap between high expenditures and economic normalization. Perhaps equally important was the opportunity for citizens to contribute to the war effort while saving funds to meet future needs. Bond purchases through payroll deductions were also effective. This was a win-win solution that could also be employed to fight global warming.

With the private sector leading crisis-level climate action, it is appropriate to draw support from all potential fund sources. Expanded climate action has been a plea from private citizens for literally decades. A long-term bond program would offer convenient opportunities for each citizen to make personal contributions and/or investments. The global potential for such citizen involvement is unknown, but is perhaps immense. Over the period before 2035, private sources could add trillions of dollars.

Long term bonds to fight global warming would be a wise investment for all segments of the private sector (plus national and local governments) because everyone would benefit from climate threat reduction and reduced climate disaster costs (not to mention lives and habitats saved).

Finally, grants to crisis-level climate action would be especially helpful during the CPA's formative years. Even small donations would demonstrate public commitment to fight global warming, and these donations would help ensure ultimate success. The long delay in decisive climate action has been a frustration to many. Opportunities to support crisis-level climate action might help vent that frustration. Credible reasons for optimism should further confidence that such support will make a difference in battling global warming.

Beyond monetary contributions and investments, there are in-kind actions that would help speed progress towards zero carbon emissions. For example, reductions in discretionary air travel can have a huge impact on global emissions. This was proven during the COVID-19 pandemic, when air travel was largely replaced by virtual communications. Listed below are various steps individuals can take to accelerate progress towards zero carbon emissions:

**Join commuter car pools and use public transportation.

**Limit vacation travel to mostly home states and neighboring regions.

**Consolidate local errands for fewer trips.

**Turn down heating thermostat.

**Turn up air conditioning thermostat.

**Turn off TVs and lights not being used.

**Take shorter and less frequent hot showers.

**Replace incandescent and fluorescent lighting with LED lighting.

**Reduce gas-powered tool use.

**Stop burning trash outdoors.

**Plant at least 12 trees (of indigenous varieties) per year per person.

Chapter 11 Sources

1. Hal Bernton, James Bruggers, "A Former Apple Orchard Could Hold the Future of Clean Hydrogen Energy in Washington," The Seattle Times, April 16, 2021, pp. A1, A7 (I3069)
2. Jack Ewing, "Daimler Aims to Drop Diesel for Hydrogen," New York Times, May 24, 2021, pp. B1, B2 (I3088)
3. Staff, "Net Zero by 2050: A Roadmap for the Global Energy Sector," International Energy Agency (press release), May 18, 2021, pp. 1-4 (I3086)
4. Niraj Chokshi, Clifford Krauss, "The Airline Industry May Not be Able to Reduce Greenhouse Gas Emissions for Decades", New York Times, June 2, 2021, pp. B1, B5 (I3093)
5. Staff, "AIRBUS$_{e}$," Airbus Website, June 18, 2021, pp. 1-4 (I3103)
6. Staff, "Green Steel," The Economist, May 15, 2021, pp. 44-45 (I3085)

7. Staff, "Toothpaste in Your Tank," The Economist, February 27, 2021, pp. 65-66 (I3018)

8. Ivan Penn, Clifford Krauss, "California Pushes a Hydrogen Economy," New York Times, November 14, 2020, pp. B1, B7 (I2929)

9. Somini Sengupta et al., "In an Australian Project, a Second Life for Coal," New York Times, August 16, 2019, pp. 1, 8 (I2621)

10. OPEC Secretariat, "World Oil Outlook, 2017 (Table 2.7: India Primary Energy)," OPEC, October 1, 2017 (I2668)

11. Lisa Friedman, "Warning of a 'Catastrophe' With the Use of Fossil Fuels, New York Times, March 22, 2022, p. A6 (I3146)

12. Brad Plumer, Raymond Zong, "Fossil Fuels Must Be Cut Faster, Panel Warns, New York Times, April 5, 2022, pp. 1,6 (I3149)

13. Philip Verleger, David G. Victor, "In Europe, the War Is Spurring Advances in Clean Energy", New York Times, April 21, 2022, p. A23 (I3159)

Chapter 12: A Time for Renewal

Introduction

Society is in a deep funk. Suicides and substance abuse are up. Hope and optimism are more rare. Homelessness is up. Affordable housing is down. Urban crime is up. Safe neighborhoods are down. Climate disasters are up. Crisis-level climate action is still waiting for political consensus and commitment. Government and personal debt is up. Savings for future needs are down. Negative news is up. Positive news is increasingly rare.

No wonder flight attendants are being attacked by passengers. Road rage is becoming more extreme. School boards are facing angry crowds. Street demonstrations are more common and more destructive. The U.S. Capitol has been brutally attacked by angry rioters. Society is in a really bad mood. But maybe the situation is worse than just a sour mood?

Looking further into society's situation, one problem mentioned in the above narrative is selected for greater focus: road rage. Road rage in relation to human brain functions was discussed briefly in Chapter 9 (Human Fallibility section). Under stress conditions, the amygdala in the lower brain issues a command for a chemical release that shuts down prefrontal cortex control (the control of responsible thinking, etc.). This allows primitive instincts to take control. But why is 21st-century behavior not better when it comes to control of stress, and why should traffic situations turn hostile?

Surely, civilized people can do better. Road rage seems barbaric, juvenile, pointless, anti-social, petty, and unhealthy. This chapter is titled "A Time for Renewal." Road rage is one sign that it is time for society to give serious consideration to comprehensive renewal.

There are other signs of the need for renewal. A second one is the long list of unsolved problems in the Preface that continue to fester when there is little expectation of progress towards solutions. Society seems preoccupied with the bad news of the day, as demonstrated by the priorities of major news outlets. Breakthrough *solutions* are rarely heard. This situation is probably a major factor behind the collective deep funk. Societal mood and behavior would likely improve with greater attention to problem solving. Crisis-level climate action could be an important step towards societal renewal.

Beyond the climate crisis, the Preface mentioned two examples of dangerous mismanagement of Earth's affairs:

(a) Overfishing wild stocks to the point of no return.

(b) Keeping nuclear weapons on continuous "launch-on-warning" alert.

These two situations were characterized in the Preface. Clearly, these are dangerous problems warranting immediate solution. They also typify dangerous situations that are below the radar of public issues tracked daily by the news media. These two problems might make good candidates for societal focus on needed and plausible solutions. Plausibility is addressed in the next section.

Renewal Through Problem Solving

Crisis-level climate action was suggested above as an important problem-solving step towards societal renewal. Chapter 11 demonstrated plausible pathways to reducing carbon emissions and combating climate threats. In some respects, the results of those potential actions were shown to be win-win for all involved parties. Further, these climate actions would help enable long-term global climate security. Such successes in climate problem solving could bolster global optimism and help elevate public moods. Likewise, successes in solving other critical problems could reinforce the positive results of crisis-level climate action. Two problems selected above were the overfishing and nuclear alert situations. The plausibility of their potential solutions is addressed in the following paragraphs.

Of these two problems, the nuclear alert situation is the least complex and easiest to solve. To review this situation, nuclear-tipped, land-based

Intercontinental Ballistic Missiles (ICBMs) are on 24/7 alert, to be launched immediately against an enemy upon warning of an incoming missile attack. As explained in the Preface, a misread warning or one faked by a hacker could trigger a nuclear weapons exchange, killing millions. The real possibility of a false or faked warning cannot be reasonably excluded.

The remedy is simple and quick. A U.S. presidential executive order could terminate the 24/7 alert policy and replace it with, say, a 3-day alert policy. The 3-day buffer would provide time to determine with certainty whether an attack warning was true or false. It should be mentioned that U.S. nuclear forces (including command and control systems) are designed and hardened to withstand a nuclear attack. Thus, a 3-day delay in launching a counterattack would not compromise the ability to retaliate.

Before announcing a change in nuclear alert policy, it might be wise for the U.S. to notify other nuclear weapon states and suggest the new policy be multilateral. Whether or not other nations took comparable actions, the U.S. action would still be in the best interests of national and global security.

Suppose no action was taken to solve the "hair trigger" nuclear alert problem. What are potential consequences of leaving the U.S. alert policy at 24/7? A plausible scenario is summarized below:

"A clever but deranged hacker breaks into the electronic U.S. missile warning and launch control systems and fakes an incoming missile attack. The hacker further generates an electronic 'authorization to launch' command to the ICBMs poised in their silos. A large ICBM salvo is launched against Russia. Russia detects the incoming missile attack and launches a counterattack against preselected targets, including the U.S. Capitol, the Pentagon and the U.S. nuclear submarine support network."

This tragic outcome of the 24/7 alert policy could be avoided with an alternative 3-day buffer policy. The difference in deterrent value is likely zero. In any case, It is asserted that a difference in deterrent value cannot be proven because deterrence, itself, cannot be proven because reasons for not acting (being deterred) are logically not provable.

The launch-on-warning policy has no positive net worth to national security, but potentially has negative net worth. A shift of policy to a 3-day or similar buffer has a likely positive gain in national security. That gain would be reduced risks of nuclear war, no matter how slight the odds.

It is asserted that the above narrative is sufficient justification to abandon the current launch-on-warning policy. Many others have made similar arguments. Yet, the current 24/7 policy continues without any serious challenge or even discussion. This state of inaction should be alarming for a serious problem easily solved. Society is allowing itself to be exposed to unnecessary risks. How many other dangerous situations are likewise continuing due to a state of inaction? Does anyone care? Is apathy a root problem? These are the kind of questions to ask when wondering whether this a time for societal renewal.

The second problem is the overfishing situation (also characterized in the Preface). This is one of the most dangerous problems on the planet—especially to life, livelihood and global economic security. It is also one of the most complex situations because of (1) conflicting sovereign interests and (2) lawlessness in the open seas (beyond sovereign boundaries). There is no magic bullet to resolve all issues. The best hope is to make incremental progress at resolving issues. Such progress might be tied to societal renewal.

There are numerous groups and entities that are stakeholders in the overfishing situation. This is a good place to look for ideas on how to make incremental progress. For example, the tuna fishing industry is trying to balance the pros and cons of fish-aggregating devices (FADS). These devices are also used to maximize illegal catches. FADS issues are rich in opportunities for making incremental progress towards reducing the risks of overfishing. These opportunities should be pursued aggressively.

Illegal fishing is a large part of the overfishing problem, and it should be targeted for making incremental progress. Legal stakeholders should join forces to promote ways to make illegal fishing unprofitable. One idea offered by this author is summarized below:

This is a scheme to certify legal catches so they can be marketed as such. If restaurants, fish markets, and supermarket fish counters offered "certified wild" to customers, the market for illegal catches would likely shrink substantially.

A scheme to certify wild catches would be based on technology. First, the industry would establish an organizational entity that supported the certification process. A generic name could be "Fishing Certification Service (FCS)." A boat that intended to limit its activity to legal fishing would register with FCS. Before leaving harbor, the boat would be issued a 25-digit certification code by FCS to be used to certify its entire catch. FCS would be supplied with a summary of the boat's expected itinerary. The certification code, in scrambled format, would be added to the boat's transponder output. Tracking systems (with unscrambling algorithms) would be able to track all certified boats (uncertified boats are left out of the certified system). When the boat returns to harbor (or offloads to a certified processing boat) the entire catch would be certified. FCS would monitor the whole process to point of sale. FCS would also certify restaurants, fish markets, etc. that displayed the "Certified Wild "seal (logo). This scenario is one possibility for how technology could ensure that a catch was truly certified and uncertified catches were excluded from many markets.

Solutions to critical problems like climate change, unsafe nuclear weapons alerts, and dangerous overfishing would demonstrate momentum toward a better future. Even engagement in the challenges of problem solving should help lift moods and give credence to optimism in the future. These should be reason enough to pursue problem solving in the context of societal renewal.

Notes on Sovereignty

It was noted earlier that competing sovereign interests complicate the overfishing situation. If national sovereignty issues were removed from this situation, then much of the complexity would likely evaporate. There is a lesson here: sovereign interests are competing with global security interests. This phenomenon was mentioned in the Chapter 7 discussion of deforestation and Chapter 9 discussion of institutional inertia. The point to remember is that sovereign interests are a common denominator that runs through much of what challenges the welfare and security of the global community.

This last point deserves further comment. Earth is home to the habitat for all life on the planet and is also home to the community of sovereign nations. Logically, what is bad for the global community is likely also bad for at least some sovereign states. If sovereignty itself is a problem for the global community, then it follows that sovereign states will suffer from that global problem (along with its citizens). Thus, sovereign nations and its citizens cannot escape problems that sovereignty itself causes the global community. This is a simple fact.

Society should consider how to redefine governance such that sovereignty is not a liability to the global community. One possibility might be to limit the authority of national sovereignty and transfer the difference to a higher authority. Perhaps society should experiment with various potential solutions to governance?

Leveraging that thought, society should consider experimentation as a powerful and safe tactic in finding solutions to any and all global problems. Society always has the option to cancel an experiment and return to the original state when an experiment fails to deliver the progress intended. Experiments can also be modified to explore alternatives. Such flexibility would be an asset in a renewed society

A good example of grass-roots experimentation is the concept of "citizen assemblies," started in Ireland to discuss current issues.[1] Citizen assemblies have also been held in France (to discuss climate action) and Chile (to discuss pension reform and health care). Additional citizen assemblies have been held in Britain, Canada, and the Netherlands. This early momentum holds promise for long-term opportunities to engage the public in the practice of democracy.

More Reasons for Renewal

Two situations were mentioned earlier as signs that society is due for renewal: hostile road rage and the chronic problems listed in the Preface. There are more signs. But, first a general observation:

There was a time (long ago) when social problems did not go much beyond one's village. But villages expanded into territories and those territories eventually became absorbed by sovereign nations. Social problems evolved along with this expansion. So did interdependencies such as economic trade and treaties. Interdependence is undergoing a radical transformation from "nice but optional" to "necessary for global welfare and survival." A common metaphor is a "shrinking world." Unfortunately, global problem-solving is not keeping pace with the new reality that interdependency is no longer optional. The fate of nations depends on the success of global-level problem-solving, wherein sovereign interests are served by the global good. The sooner this reality is acknowledged, the better. Must this acknowledgment wait for societal renewal? If so, then that renewal must be given urgent priority.

Elaborating on the role of interdependency, COVID-19 and its evolving variants are teaching people the necessity of global vaccinations. Pandemics can either be ended through global herd immunity or continue to worsen with more aggressive variants. This is the nature of the COVID-19 pandemic.[2] If the virus is allowed to continue evolving in under-vaccinated regions, the rest of the planet remains at risk. By the end of 2021, it is estimated that high-income regions will be 75% vaccinated, whereas poor countries will be only 25% protected.[2] To their own peril, rich nations are protecting themselves while withholding sufficient aid to help poor nations protect themselves.

This situation is hard evidence of a society in urgent need of renewal. Current society seems deaf to the reality of global interdependence. Andrea Taylor, Assistant Director of Duke Global Health Innovation Center, observes: "This idea that no one is safe until everyone is safe is not just an adage, it is really true."[2.]

The second sign has to do with detachment from reality. The sign discussed above is just one example of this detachment.

According to a survey conducted by Monmouth University, 77% of those who voted for Donald Trump in the 2020 presidential election believe election fraud put Joe Biden in the White House.[3] This is despite the fact that multiple audits of that election could not find significant evidence of election fraud. Disbelief in scientific evidence proving human evolution is another case of detachment from reality. Interviewed participants in the January 6 attack on the U.S. Capitol claim patriotism as a motivation-another disconnect with reality. The extreme popularity of fantasy movies, games, and books is evidence of the social need to escape from reality.

This discussion of social detachment from reality concludes with two gross examples: (1) the broad movement to defund police and (2) the net-zero climate goal to continue carbon pollution to 2050 and beyond.

The movement to defund police, underscored by numerous street demonstrations, proves a significant disconnect with reality. This movement was motivated by unacceptable behavior on the part of an extremely small percentage of police officers. The reality is the vast majority of police officers are honoring the oaths they have taken and are providing necessary services to their communities. Another reality is the strong correlation between rising crime and shrinking police department budgets. The defunding movement was out of touch with reality and communities are paying the price with unsafe neighborhoods and compromised police protection.

Wide acceptance of the net-zero emissions goal by 2050 demonstrates an unfortunate disconnect between society and reality. The impracticability of the 2050 net-zero goal was discussed in Chapter 10. The current reality is that a zero-emissions goal is already long overdue. Society has known about global warming since the early '80s and some have understood the gravity of the threat since the late '80s. A zero-emissions goal should have been set then for, say, 2005 (a plausible goal for a much lower starting point in global emissions). Society is still out of touch with climate reality and is paying the price in lost lives, extinct species, destroyed habitats, worsening weather, and still-climbing disaster costs.

The case for societal renewal is now paused for society's consideration.

Gazing into the Distant Future

What does the future hold? Humanity's journey into the future is headed into uncharted territory. To a limited extent, the future is what society chooses to pursue. Perhaps a populated habitat on the Moon? Water and ice have been discovered there, and the lower gravity would be advantageous for launching deep space missions or missions within our solar system. Will we encounter alien life as we venture into space? It seems aliens are already visiting us here and are maybe signaling "no threat" with playful behavior.[4,5]

Gazing deeper into space and time, here are some tentative predictions:

Society will become much better at managing its affairs.

Science and technology will discover how to move quickly through space, perhaps using gravity waves or the energy emanating from black holes.

Psychic phenomena will become better understood, become a science, and become useful to humanity.

In the item above, replace "psychic" with "spiritual"

(This is left blank because the key words are not yet in current vocabularies)

Ditto above.

Humanity's journey into the future will be the pleasure of coming generations.

Bon voyage!

Chapter 12 Sources

1. Staff, "Some Assembly Required," The Economist, September 19, 2020, pp. 57-58. (I2900)
2. Lynsey Chutel, Marc Santora, "Posing Global Threat, Variants Spread Where Vaccines Have Not," New York Times, February 1, 2021, pp. 1, 6 (I2995)
3. Jen Schwartz, "Reestablishing Reality," Scientific American, February 2021, pp. 37, 39 (I2996)
4. Helene Cooper, et al., " 'Wow, What is That?' Navy Pilots Reported Unexplained Flying Objects," New York Times, May 27, 2019, p. A14 (I3106)
5. Courtney Kube, Adam Edelman, "UFO Report: Government Can't Explain 143 of 144 Mysterious Flying Objects, Blames Limited Data," NBC News, June 25, 2021, pp. 1-4 (I3105)

Printed in the USA
CPSIA information can be obtained
at www.ICGtesting.com
CBHW051556310324
6137CB00024BA/2059